COMMERCIAL
CUT FLOWER
PRODUCTION

Grower Guide No. 2
2nd Series

Grower Books
Nexus Media Limited, Kent

Grower Books
Nexus Media Limited
Nexus House
Swanley, Kent BR8 8HU

First published 1997
Reprinted 1998

© Grower Books 1998

ISBN 1 899372 11 3

Series editor Peter Rogers.   Production Octavia Wolton.
Publisher Tony Salter.

Printed in Great Britain.

Due care has been taken in the preparation of this book. The information is based on standard insutry practice as interpreted by the author; it should not be regarded as a complete production programme nor as the only suitable regime. The publisher and author will not accept responsibility for any outcome arising from the application of the information it contains.

Contents

The publishers acknowledge with thanks the help of:

Philip Bailey of Hamer Seeds for supplying photographs of antirrhinums, asters, eustoma, limonium, molucella, stocks, trachelium.

John Whetman of HR Whetman & Son for his contribution to the chapter on pinks (Chapter 13) and for the photographs on pages 58 & 59.

Abbreviations used in this book

m = metre
cm = centimetre
sq m = square metre
g = gram

General notes

Most of the crops in this book require a growing temperature during winter of a minimum of 10C. Temperatures during propagation (where appropriate) are specified in the text.

A short day, unless specifically defined is normally less than eight hours; a long day more than 14 hours.

The cut flower market

The cut flower markets in Europe is dominated by chrysanthemums, roses and carnations. This book is concerned with 16 alternative types.

Crops such as alstroemerias and gerberas have been around for many years, but improved varieties and growing techniques have made them increasingly attractive to growers. Other crops have emerged from attempts to grow traditional outdoor types under protection, asters and antirrhinums for example.

There are, in fact, ample opportunities for summer flowers to be grown under glass or plastic; some, like eustoma and bouvardia, have already made a substantial impact while others, like liatris and limonium, are still to be fully exploited.

The level of investment required to start growing the crops described in this book varies enormously. To buy in stocks of new varieties of, say, gerbera or alstroemeria, can be a major item in itself; labour and fuel bills can quickly add to this.

On the other hand flowers traditionally grown outdoors, like annual asters, can be grown at much lower cost and with little labour until the crop is harvested.

The economics of a new crop are not simple, however, and can only really be determined by experience. It is not safe to predict returns on the basis of the previous year's data and when considering an alternative crop the grower has to take several factors into consideration.

The first factor is marketing. There is no point growing flowers no one wants to buy. Secondly, while many of the crops described are modest in terms of production facilities, labour can be important. Shorter term crops in particular need little labour input until harvesting when the manpower needed can be considerable.

The key to consumer acceptance is vase life. The attractiveness of blooms is obviou but it is the length of time they remain attractive which determines whether the retailer or the consumer will come back for more.

1 Alstroemeria

Perennial, for planting June-July for flowering
April-June and September-November the following year

Alstroemeria, the Peruvian Lily, is a crop which is still increasing in acreage and market demand both in Europe and worldwide. It has recently gained a place in the top ten list of cut flowers produced in Holland. Alstroemeria plants are propagated by division of the fleshy rhizomes which make up the root system, and a crop is usually grown for one or two years for cut flower production before being cleared and replanted, although some recent introductions may be worth cropping for three or even four years.

A good range of high-yielding alstroemeria varieties has become available in the last few years as a result of intensive breeding programmes in Holland. Most of these are protected by the suppliers, and available only on a contract basis, with no vegetative propagation permitted from the flowering stock. Some older varieties are now unrestricted. Varieties which are most widely grown at present include Flamengo, Jubilee, Tiara, Victoria, Yellow King, Marina, Pink Triumph, Rosario and Cavalier, although there are many others.

Several new introductions appear on the scene every year. Recent additions include Rebecca, with large bicoloured rose and white flowers and better overall quality than Rosario, and two salmon pink varieties, Java and Aruba.

Two white hybrids with pink markings have just been released, Petronella and Capri. The latter, like several other recent introductions, is a true year-round variety with no lighting requirement for winter production. Toscana is an unusually-coloured carmine variety with good winter quality.

So far none of the new varieties can really claim a substantial increase in winter production and this continues to be a problem with alstroemeria.

The first mini alstroemeria for cut flower production has just been released, too.

Called Little Star, it has yellow flowers with darker markings. It has half-sized flowers but more flowers per stem. Orange and red versions are expected soon.

The vigour and production level of particular varieties should be checked with the suppliers. There is a wide range of ultimate plant height, from 1.5m or less to around 2.5m. The length of the cut stem can range from 80 to 120cm or more. Yield can vary between 150 and 300 stems/sq m of glasshouse area from a well-grown soil crop.

Production cycles

The most usual planting time for alstroemerias is from late September to early November, although this depends on the variety. Some are suitable for planting at any time of the year, while others need to be established during the early summer. It is important in the case of the less strongly growing varieties that planting should not be too late because good root development is needed before light and temperature levels fall in the winter. Conversely the more vigorous varieties benefit from planting quite late. Early planting of these varieties leads to over-rapid establishment and adds to the work load with no increase in production.

Older varieties of alstroemeria bloom in flushes, twice a year. The first and usually larger flush commences in April and continues through May and into early June. The plants then rest for a few weeks and come back with a lighter flush in the autumn or winter. The second flush is more variable and a few older varieties may occasionally fail to produce a second crop at all. Many of the products of recent breeding programmes are described as year-round. They still flush, but they have more reliable winter production than the older varieties, as well as better winter quality.

Traditionally alstroemeria crops are kept in production for two or three years although they are sometimes terminated after the first flush in their second year to allow a longer turn-round time for re-planting. The second and subsequent years' growth, particularly of some of the older, more vigorous varieties is rather tall and it is sometimes better to take only the first season's production and then re-plant.

ESTABLISHMENT

Alstroemerias are usually grown in the soil, although work in Holland has shown that the crop can be grown very well in both peat and perlite. Rockwool and expanded clay granules were less successful in Dutch trials.

Alstroemerias require a loose, open substrate which is free-draining. The crop is deep-rooting and soil cultivation down to at least 50cm is necessary. If there is a water table above this level, then a drainage system will need to be installed.

Adequate organic material should be incorporated into the soil to provide a good rooting medium. Farmyard manure is suitable but should be well rotted, and properly mixed in by means of a rotary cultivator.

Alstroemerias prefer a fairly acid substrate and may grow less well if the soil pH is higher than 6.5. A more alkaline soil can be improved by using peat as a soil conditioner, without adding lime, as peat has an acidifying effect on the substrate. A coarse peat is most suitable since it has the best effect on the structure.

Planting

Minimal base fertilisers are necessary under normal glasshouse conditions once the pH has been brought within the correct range. Unless soil analysis shows any particular nutritional deficiency a general compound fertiliser can be used at about one tonne/acre. If high salt levels occur in the soil, these have first to be reduced by leaching with clear water. A planting hole should be made into which the root ball is set, with the top level with the soil surface. The root ball should have been watered prior to planting and the plant settled in with a hose watering immediately afterwards.

Spacing and support

Plant spacing for alstroemerias in the growing house should be between 3 and 3.5 plants/sq m of glasshouse according to variety. Strongly growing varieties benefit from the wider spacing and plant suppliers will be able to offer advice on suitable plant density.

Because the plants reach a final height of anything up to 2.5m it is important that the crop is properly supported. Galvanised mesh is most commonly used and four or even five layers are necessary to keep the crop under control through two or three years of growth. Mesh of 12.5cm is best for the two lower layers, although 20cm netting is sometimes used. For the top layers 20cm mesh is satisfactory and has the advantage that harvesting is easier through the wider mesh.

All the layers of netting should be put down on the floor at planting time and gradually raised as the crop develops. In this way the plants are supported cleanly at all times. If additional layers have to be added over the growing crop there is the danger that shoots will be damaged and the operation of pulling the growth through the newly added support is quite labour intensive.

The vertical supports to which the layers of netting are attached should be tall enough and rigid enough to cope with the eventual height and weight of the crop; the top layer of netting should be raised to at least 1m above the bed. Once a flush has been harvested the layers of netting should be lowered so that they can again be raised progressively as the next blooms develop.

CROP CULTURE

During the first few weeks after planting the main priority should be to ensure good establishment and root development.

Temperature regime

Water should be given to maintain a fairly uniform soil moisture level and the minimum night air temperature should be kept up to 16C or more in the case of early plantings and to at least 14C for the later-planted more vigorous varieties.

Once the plants are well established the temperatures should be reduced to their normal winter level. This depends on the available light. In the UK and Holland a temperature of around 10-12C should be maintained, particularly after warm days in the late autumn. In the darkest weather of December and January, particularly in more northern situations, a minimum temperature of 8C is acceptable. This pattern of temperatures should be repeated for subsequent years of growth in the case of older crops.

As the spring flush develops the temperatures are allowed to rise, but at no time should the soil temperature be permitted to exceed 20C, particularly once the first flush is over. This is because higher summer temperatures encourage the plants to become dormant which in turn delays and weakens the autumn/winter flush.

It is not usually necessary to shade the crop unless it is impossible to avoid extreme climatic conditions which would otherwise cause leaf scorch. Some older varieties are more sensitive than others and these should be shaded in bright sun. Experiments have shown that any reduction in light intensity is likely to result in a reduction in quality under north European conditions, so shading should be used sparingly.

Soil cooling has been tried experimentally on alstroemerias in Holland but with variable results. Keeping the summer soil temperature down to 13-15C without resorting to shading improved the percentage of good quality flowering stems with some varieties, but in many cases it also lowered total shoot production.

Watering, nutrition and CO2

Active plant growth must be maintained all the time, otherwise leaf scorch will occur and quality will suffer. Even in the winter water uptake and transpiration must be encouraged by keeping a uniform soil temperature and moisture content. Air humidity should be kept down to 80-85% as much as possible, even if this means applying heat and ventilation together in dull, calm conditions.

Alstroemerias should be generously watered when they are in active growth, especially while the spring flush is developing. Little work has been done on the nutritional needs of this crop, but as a general guide a high nitrogen feed should be used until the end of the spring flush, switching to a higher potassium feed to strengthen the foliage for the autumn and winter. Regular low strength feeding is preferable to less frequent strong feeds.

Carbon dioxide enrichment has been tried on alstroemerias, but it is unlikely to be economic unless the carbon dioxide is available as a by-product of the heating installation. In Holland, 1000 vpm of carbon dioxide is used during the heating season and this appears to advance the spring flush, although claims that either yield or flower quality is increased are less convincing.

Good flower quality can only be achieved if there is good light and air access through the crop and this requires that the weak growth within the beds is removed from time to time. As soon as the crop is established in December or January, the weak shoots should be cut out to leave 20 to 30 strong shoots/sq m to form the spring flush.

Coming into the second winter this operation becomes even more important as dense growth develops in the autumn. Delaying this thinning operation means that too much material has to be removed at one time and this weakens the plants and reduces yields.

Daylength lighting

Alstroemerias are daylength sensitive and a flush can often be advanced in short day conditions by providing supplementary lighting. It is necessary to lengthen the days sufficiently to produce the desired effect, but without excessive use of the lights.

This is because longer than optimum daylength will reduce both the rate of shoot extension and the number of buds on the stem, particularly under high temperature conditions. Several recently-introduced hybrids flower well without lights in the winter and lighting should not be used on these.

Lighting should be from either a fluorescent or an incandescent light source at the rate of about 15 watts/sq m of glasshouse. The lights should be placed high enough over the crop so that all plants receive a similar level of illumination, because poorly distributed lighting will lead to very uneven growth in the crop.

Lighting for advancing and synchronising the autumn crop should begin any time after the middle of August, as natural daylength reduces to below about 14 hours. If the crop is to be grown on for another season, daylength should be held at about 13 hours. Theoretically the extension of daylength to initiate buds needs to continue for only two to three weeks, but in practice greater uniformity can be achieved by continuing lighting for rather longer.

To light for the spring flush, the technique can be continued until natural daylength reaches 13 hours, having started during January as soon as plants are showing good shoot development. To advance the final flush before clearing the crop it is sometimes justified to increase the daylength at the expense of some stem length. In this situation up to 15 hours may be used or even 16 hours in the case of tall varieties.

Two techniques can be used to reduce the consumption of electricity without reducing the effect of lighting. These are night-break lighting and cyclic lighting and both can be used with alstroemerias. Cyclic lighting, using incandescent lights switched on for 10 minutes in every half hour, is widely used in Holland.

Bud abortion

Although lighting alstroemerias with low levels of artificial illumination encourages the initiation of buds through the plant's daylength response, it does not prevent the drying up or abortion of buds during poor light periods of growth.

Buds sometimes fail to develop fully in the winter, especially if growth is dense and light transmission to the shoots is poor. This is an effect of overall light levels, which need to be far greater than the level of artificial illumination given to extend the daylength.

Because of this problem it is not wise to use supplementary lighting to modify the flowering time of the crop if to do this involves bud development in poor natural light. Lighting for the spring flush should therefore not start before the end of

December or early January according to the natural light levels expected in the early spring months. Consequently, even in the best winter light areas the spring flush cannot safely be forced to start earlier than about the end of February.

HARVESTING

Alstroemerias have a vase life of at least two weeks if they are properly harvested and handled. This vase life is one of the most important attractions of alstroemerias to the consumer, so every effort must be made to maximise it.

The correct stage to cut the stems for the wholesale market is when the buds are showing colour and about to open. For direct sale, harvesting can be delayed until the first flowers have just opened. Harvesting prematurely carries the risk that some buds may fail to develop fully, which in turn reduces the vase life.

It is possible in some circumstances to break off the stems from the root rather than cut them. Breaking is less likely to be satisfactory than cutting if the soil is light or if the root system is weak because plants will be damaged and slow to grow away to the next flush.

Alstroemerias should not be left out of water longer than necessary, otherwise vase life will be reduced. As soon as the blooms have been transported to the packing shed they should stand in deep water preferably with a flower conditioning material added. Subsequent bud opening will be improved if the stems are stored in the light. Blooms can be held for a few days, if necessary, in a refrigerated store at a temperature of 1C.

Foliage yellowing

One of the commonest quality problems of alstroemeria is a tendency for the foliage to turn yellow after harvesting. To some extent this is being resolved by plant breeding, with several of the recent introductions being quite resistant to foliage yellowing. The problem has also been reduced experimentally by using growth regulators in the vase solution, but this is unlikely to be commercially practicable.

Alstroemerias are normally sold in bunches of 10 and should be transported and presented in the market wrapped in polythene film to protect the foliage from damage.

Grading standards for alstroemerias depend on the market's requirements. As a rule, it should be based on the number of flowers on the stem. The top grade, for example, can require a minimum of five flowers and successive lower grades proportionally less. Even blooms with a single flower are marketable and can be combined in a larger bunch appropriately marked.

PESTS AND DISEASES

Although alstroemerias have the reputation of being fairly immune to most pest and disease problems by virtue of their rapid and strong growth both above and below the ground, they nevertheless require soil sterilisation before planting if soil-borne diseases are to be avoided. A watch also has to be kept for insect pests which can mark or damage the leaves, since the cleanliness of the foliage is important to the marketability of the crop.

Alstroemerias are very sensitive to pesticides, and no material should be used unless it has been tested previously on a small area. Proper precautions should be taken to apply smoke formulations or wet sprays only when the plants are turgid and not under water stress.

Pests

Aphid colonies frequently build up towards the top of the young growth. The less vigorous varieties seem to be more commonly affected than stronger varieties. A wide range of materials and formulations are suitable for their control.

Tortrix caterpillars are recognised by the webs which the older caterpillars form in the rolled-up leaves of the crop. These webs make it difficult to reach the caterpillars with chemicals and so early treatment with insecticidal wet sprays is important.

Slugs, both large or small, can attack the young developing shoots, occasionally eating through the stem below soil level. Reducing the moisture level around the base of the plants gives a less suitable environment for the pest, and this can be followed up by chemical control.

Thrips can build up in the late summer to the extent that flecked foliage can reduce the market value of the crop. As with aphids, the more vigorous varieties are less seriously attacked. Chemical control measures should be the same as for aphids.

Diseases

The fungal disease botrytis causes the well-known grey mould on damaged plant material. If the crop is well-grown botrytis should seldom be serious however. The crop should be kept well ventilated, so that the foliage does not remain wet for long periods, especially at night.

In spells of humid weather a boost of pipe heat first thing in the day can reduce the level of early morning condensation in which botrytis thrives. If chemical control becomes necessary a wide range of fungicidal sprays are available. If the infection of the crop is close to ground level it is possible to spray only the base of the plants, thus avoiding the risk of marking the foliage of the flower stems.

If good soil hygiene, structure and moisture content allow vigorous root growth in the early stages of crop establishment, root rots should seldom be a serious problem. The normal range of fungicidal soil drenches appear to be quite safe on alstroemerias provided they are put on to moist soil.

One or two virus diseases producing a mottle of the leaves have been found on alstroemerias. These are apparently transmitted in the soil by eelworms and so it is particularly important to use an effective soil sterilant (chemical or steam) between crops if virus symptoms have been observed. Alstroemerias are very sensitive to paraquat weedkillers and these should not be used in the vicinity of the crop where there is any risk of spray drift.

Deficiency disorder

The symptoms of iron deficiency on alstroemerias are a reduction in vigour and a yellowing of the new growth. Some varieties are more often affected than others, particularly the more vigorous types. The deficiency can be corrected by the use of iron chelate as a wet spray or a soil drench, repeated after one week to ensure full uptake by the plants.

SAFETY

Some people are sensitive to the sap of alstroemerias, and may show an allergic response when working in the crop. This sensitivity has also been reported by florists handling alstroemerias regularly.

2 Antirrhinums

Annual, sow January-February to flower late April and May

Antirrhinum majus has been a credible contender for commercial cut flower production since the first range of F1 hybrid varieties was developed as a result of breeding work 15 to 20 years ago in the United States (where incidentally the crop is invariably known as spandragons or snaps) but interest is still limited in the UK. F1 hybrid lines, which are now available in a wide range of colours, are often classified according to their preferences for light intensity and daylength.

Four response groups of antirrhinums are recognised in the US and varieties for cultivation at particular times of the year can be selected from the appropriate group.

F1 varieties for glasshouse cropping in Europe include the early hybrid range Tattoo, available in individual or mixed colours for spring flowering and the Bouquet series, which is not quite so early, but which can cope with higher temperatures at flowering time. Bouquet is therefore ideal for late spring or summer production. Other popular individual F1 hybrids include Snowman (white), Golden Spike (yellow), Vulcan (red) and Jackpot (pink). The F1 Rocket series is more suitable for outdoor production from a mid March or April sowing date.

PROPAGATION

Hybrid antirrhinums are raised from seed. The seed is very fine, about 7,000/g and so it is necessary to use a fine, free-draining compost which retains both water and air in suitable proportions.

The compost must be sterile and should be well moistened before sowing. Antirrhinum seedlings are very sensitive to high salt levels and it is important that the compost should remain moist and that nutrient levels should be low, particularly in the case of organic nitrogen.

A standard seed tray will take around 0.1 gram of seed and will produce about 300 to 350 seedlings suitable for pricking off.

The optimum germination temperature for antirrhinums is 20C. The first seedlings will be visible in five to six days. During this stage the trays should be covered to retain maximum humidity and compost moisture. If the compost dries out on the surface emergence will be delayed and germinated plants can suffer damage.

As soon as the first seedlings are seen the trays should be uncovered and the temperature dropped to 15C. The humidity should be lower from then on to reduce the risk of fungal rots developing on the young plants and the compost moisture level should also be carefully managed.

Sowing schedule

The sowing date is dependent on the cropping schedule. For example, plants for late April or May flowering should be sown in December and planted out in the New Year. For winter flowering of suitable varieties, the sowing date should be between late July and the first week of August. A late June sowing will come into production from the middle of October.

CROP CULTURE

Seedlings are usually pricked off after four to six weeks, planting directly into the border soil of the cropping house, although it is possible to go through an intermediate stage in peat blocks or squares if this is more convenient. The usual planting density is around 40 to 45 plants/sq m of glasshouse and this can be achieved by putting one plant in each square of a layer of 12.5 x12.5cm netting, which will eventually be raised to provide support for the crop.

Antirrhinums need a free-draining soil with a pH between 6.5 and 7 for optimum growth and the soil should be clean and free from weeds. It may be sufficient to have sterilised before the previous crop if no problems have been encountered.

Because antirrhinums are particularly sensitive to high salt levels in the soil it is not usual to feed the crop after planting so soil analysis should be carried out before planting to see if any base fertilisers are needed or excess salts have to be removed. If excessive salts are present the growth of the crop will quickly become stunted and the leaves will begin to roll inwards.

Minor nutrients

Both calcium and boron deficiency symptoms are common in antirrhinums. The former problem can cause whole plants to die back and the latter shows up as necrosis of the flower buds in the later stages of their development. Both elements should be available in sufficient quantity before planting and a further application of boron, as a foliar spray, may be necessary prior to flowering.

Temperature regimes

The size and strength of the flower stem is strongly dependent on growing temperature. The lower the temperature the more vigorous the growth.

For the first three or four weeks after planting a temperature of 15-17C by night will ensure that flowering is not excessively delayed but from this stage onwards a night temperature of 10C should be the target, with day temperatures reaching no higher than 18C in sunny weather.

Higher temperatures reduce flower quality considerably and it may be necessary to shade summer crops to avoid this. Conversely, in the winter the crop will grow perfectly well at 5C or even lower, the only problem being the considerable delay in flowering caused by very low temperatures.

Carbon dioxide enrichment may have a marginal effect on flower quality but is of doubtful economic benefit. It appears not to advance the time of flowering and any effect it does have is more likely to be apparent in high temperature conditions in summer, when its application is in any case less practicable.

Daylength lighting

Antirrhinums will bloom in any daylength, but the time to flowering is shorter in long day conditions. Because of this there is interest in the possibility of shortening the growing period with supplementary lighting, although this cannot be recommended on a commercial basis until the economics of the technique are clearer.

If it is necessary to shorten the time from planting to flowering during the winter months in order to fit in with an overall cropping schedule, this should be done primarily with extra heating. Two-hour night break lighting could also be tried on an experimental basis, using incandescent bulbs as for year-round chrysanthemum culture.

Watering

Antirrhinums should be watered with care, because the plants are susceptible to botrytis rot. It is equally important that the crop should not be short of water at any time, particularly when growth is rapid approaching the flowering stage.

If liquid feeding is applied to the crop at any time it should be followed by an application of clear water to minimise the risk of salt build-up.

Pinching

When the plants have reached a height of about 30cm they can be pinched down to three pairs of leaves. The sidebreaks will each develop a strong flower stem. Any weak shoots should be removed as a separate operation to channel the plant's resources into potentially marketable stems.

Italian research indicates that pinching and shooting in this way will give an economic advantage over single stem growing, even though the individual flower stems will be shorter and there will be a delay of about three weeks in flowering.

A well-grown crop can be expected to yield about 90% of first quality blooms from single stem culture; say, 35 to 40 stems/ sq m of glasshouse on a typical plant

In terms of value as a commercial crop, Alstroemeria probably ranks first among those crops covered in this book, at least in the UK. In the Netherlands it would be challenged by Gerbera. Alstroemeria is in a different league from, say, antirrhinum or stocks, being more like Chrysanthemums as a mainstream year-round glasshouse crop.

*Antirrhinums
Montezuma (above)
and Tattoo Deep
Rose (right)*

[Pictures: Hamer Flower Seeds]

*Aster Callistephus
Matsumo Purple Rose
(above) Matsumo White
(right)*

[Pictures: Hamer Flower Seeds]

Bouvardia (left) has been subject to intensive breeding programmes in the recent past which have led to higher yielding new varieties.

Campula glomerata Superba Strain, also known as 'clustered bellflower' (right)

[Picture: Hamer Flower Seeds]

Growing Delphiniums under glass for a cut flower crop calls for careful cultural management to avoid soft growth. With care, however, an acceptable product can the achieved.

Eustoma is one of the most spectacular of the 'new generation' of cut flower crops. Shown here are: Eustoma Fiji Picotee Blue Improved (top), Dream Blue Improved (above left) and Kyoto Pure White (above right)

[Pictures: Hamer Flower Seeds]

Gerberas look spectacular in a flower arrangement; they are impressive too in the type of market pack developed by the Dutch who still grow most of the blooms sold in the UK.

	Sowing period	Planting period	Harvest
ANNUALS			
Antirrhinum		Jan-Feb	Late Apr-May
Aster, Chinese	end Jun-early Jul		October
Aster ericoldes		Mar-Apr	Jul-Aug
Aster novi-belgli		Mar-early Jun	Jun-end Jul
Delphinium	mid Mar-mid May		late May-June
Eustoma		Mar-Apr	Jun-Jul
Gypsophilia elegans	Feb onwards		May onwards
Liatris		end Jan-early Feb	mid May-end June
Limonium		Feb-Apr	Apr-June
Molucella		May-Jun	Jul-Aug
Stocks		Feb-Mar	May-Jun
Trachelium		Apr	Jun-Jul
BIENNIALS			
Campanula		Dec	May
Sweet william		Sep-early Oct	May-Jun
PERENNIALS			
Alstroemeria		Jun-Jul	(1)Apr-Jun (2)Sep-Nov
Gypsophila paninculata		Mar-Apr	(1)May onwards (2)Sep-Oct
Bouvardia		lateMar-Apr	(1)Jul-Aug (2)Nov-Dec (3)Apr-May
Gerbera		end Feb-Mar	May onwards
Pinks		Aug	(1)late Apr-Nov
		Mar-Apr	(2)late Jun-Dec (3)Apr-May

spacing. Sidebreaks can be taken later but they will generally be of low quality.

Pinched plants can produce three to four first cut stems/plant. The proportion of first grade stems will be lower but total returns will probably be higher.

HARVESTING

Antirrhinums should be harvested when six to eight florets are open on the stem. The cutting stage is not critical and stems can be cut a day or two earlier or later to suit handling or marketing requirements. A typical crop will be cut over a period of two weeks, cutting twice or three times a week.

The stems should be put into deep water as soon as they have been cut, preferably containing a flower preservative.

Limited cool storage at 5C appears to have no adverse effect on vase life. The stems must be kept vertical when they are stored or packed loose, because horizontal stems turn upwards. This effect is a geotropic reaction and it occurs even in the absence of light.

PESTS AND DISEASES

The root rot fungi pythium and rhizoctonia attack antirrhinums in the early stages of growth.

Pythium is a common problem in the seed-raising stage but seldom develops if a good standard of hygiene is maintained at this time. As a precaution an appropriate fungicide can be incorporated into the seed compost.

Rhizoctonia is more likely to develop after pricking off or planting, and often attacks the stem at ground level. Careful handling of the plants can reduce the risk and proper soil sterilisation is important. If the disease is noticed, a fungicidal spray or soil drench will help control it.

In damp conditions the characteristic grey mould of botrytis can develop and spread quickly. The initial infection often occurs on damaged seedling leaves after pricking off but once established botrytis will attack both dead and healthy tissue. The primary method of control should rely on cultural techniques, keeping the crop as dry as possible by ventilating and applying heat to encourage air movement. Fungicidal dusts or wet sprays can be used to back up environmental control.

Mildew appears as a white powder on the leaves. It too spreads in high humidity conditions, and control should be cultural in the first instance, followed as necessary by chemical control measures. Some fungicidal sprays are likely to leave a residue on the crop and so are less popular for use in the later stage of the crop.

Antirrhinum rust is another occasional disease problem, more common outdoors than under glass. The symptoms are characteristic and easily recognised – brown spots on the leaves, generally surrounded by pale concentric rings. Fungicides can be applied as a preventative measure.

The most common pest problem on antirrhinums is attack from aphids, which can be controlled by wet sprays.

3 Asters

Several types of aster are used for cut flower production
and their cultural requirements differ considerably

CHINESE ASTER

Annual, sow late June - early July to flower October

The Chinese Aster, (Callistephus chinensis) is also known as the summer aster. It is an annual, which flowers in August and September outdoors. It is grown from seed and a wide range of varieties and types are available. Colours range from white, through yellow, pink and salmon to crimson and violet. The Pompon series of doubles, which have shorter stems than most other types, are particularly popular. The Matsumoto series is one of the earliest, while the Ariake series flowers later than most.

For glasshouse production, seed is usually sown in late June or early July to produce blooms in October to follow on from the outdoor crops. A gram of seeds will generate about 200 good plants.

A plant spacing of 40 to 50/sq m of glasshouse is used and net supports are needed for the taller varieties.

Callistephus is less sensitive to daylength than many other asters but it tends to produce more side breaks in long day conditions and fewer, but taller shoots, in short days. So plant spacing may need to be adjusted with this in mind.

Callistephus is very susceptible to the soilborne aster yellows virus and aster wilt and it is usually recommended that long-term crop rotations should be used to prevent the build-up of these diseases.

MICHAELMAS DAISY

Perennial, grown as Annual, plant March - early June to flower July

The Michaelmas Daisy (Aster novi-belgii) is widely grown for cut flowers. It is a perennial, grown from rooted cuttings, which are planted at 50 to 60/sq m for glasshouse production. Their general cultural requirements match those of natural season chrysanthemums which they closely resemble in many ways.

Michaelmas daisies flower naturally from August to the end of September but they can be programmed under glass to flower in late spring and early summer by using daylength control. Four weeks of short days immediately after planting, followed by long days, will produce a flush 10 to 12 weeks after planting.

ASTER ERICOIDES

Annual, plant March - April to flower July - August

Aster ericoides, also known as Aster pringlei, is best known by the popular white cultivar, Monte Cassino, although there are a number of pink, rose and blue cultivars, including Blue Wonder and the Butterfly range.

Aster ericoides is grown from rooted cuttings planted in early spring at a density of 24 to 40/sq m of glasshouse.

Short day treatment is needed to achieve good flower quality in the summer, and it is usual to shade the crop to give nine- to 10-hour days for a period of about six weeks once the plants have reached a height of 30 to 35cm – generally around mid June.

It is important to keep the temperatures and humidity levels down as low as possible under the shading, so the shading tents should be opened up for a time each night if possible. It has been shown that timing or quality is not significantly affected by shading for only six days each week – this may help with environmental control.

Shading should in any case stop when the first blooms show colour otherwise there is a risk of flowers developing brown marks caused by humidity scorch.

SOLIDASTER LUTEUS

Perennial, to flower at any time

The inter-generic hybrid Solidaster luteus is becoming increasingly popular as a glasshouse cut flower crop in Europe. It is a perennial, grown from rooted rhizome cuttings which are available in a limited range of yellow varieties.

Solidaster is moderately daylength-sensitive. It will flower irrespective of daylength but will come into bloom more quickly in short days. It should be shaded to give short days only after it has had eight weeks of daylengths above 12 hours and has reached a height of about 60cm. Flowering can start as early as four to five weeks after the start of shading. Shading can be removed for a part of the day in hot weather without much effect on crop timing.

Solidaster is sometimes infected with the crown rot disease Sclerotium rolfsii. The planting material is the most common source of infection and once established it can be very difficult to eradicate. Other common problems are leafminer and whitefly.

A few Goldenrod hybrids, Solidago species, are also grown for cut flowers. Their culture and daylength requirements are much the same as those for Solidaster.

4 Bouvardia

Perennial, plant March - April to produce three flushes a year (July - August, November - December, April - May)

Bouvardia is a cut-flower crop which is only just becoming recognised in the UK, but which has been making a big impact in Holland in recent years, and which is still expanding in acreage. The principal cause of the interest in this crop is an intensive breeding programme, which has brought a lot of high yielding new varieties on to the scene and encouraged greater investigation into their cultural requirements.

Most commercial bouvardia crops planted now are varieties developed as hybrids from the Bouvardia domestica group, although some crops of Bouvardia longiflora (white) are also grown. The latest bouvardia hybrids to become available have bigger flowers and brighter colours than the older varieties.

Winter production is higher and the plants are generally more robust, offering an extended vase life. With bouvardia it is well worth going for the best hybrids on offer.

PROPAGATION

Propagation of Bouvardia is by stem cuttings from selected mother plants. These mother plants are brought into production in February by increasing the temperature regime to 18-20C and each plant is capable of yielding up to 60 cuttings through the spring and early summer.

Cuttings are struck into small containers with a peat-based compost, using a rooting hormone, and rooted at a temperature of 20-22C in maximum humidity.

ESTABLISHMENT

The most common planting time is between the end of March and the beginning of May. In the first season of production it is possible to take two flushes if the plants are established by mid May, otherwise only one flush is possible.

It is important to build up a good plant structure both above and below the ground before a flush is taken and this is done by stopping the plants twice as they begin to grow away after the establishment period.

When the shoots reach about 30cm they are pinched down to two or three pairs of leaves, and this is repeated as the resulting basal shoots grow away after the first stopping. The basal shoots should also be stopped in this way at the start of the second year's growth, as the plants come out of their resting period.

CROP CULTURE

Soil structure and condition is very important for bouvardia, and an open soil with a high organic matter content is needed. A pH of 5.5 to 6.5 is suitable with a rather low total salt content and moderate levels of the major nutrients. The potash to nitrogen level should be higher in the autumn than in the spring.

Soil sterilisation is essential for the control of fungal root rots.

In Holland a number of growers grow the crop in large, plastic containers 15-20cm deep and filled with a peat loam mixture. It is claimed that this system of proudction gives better control of plant vigour than with direct planting in the bed and less risk of root diseases becoming established in the crop. Soilless substrates, particularly rockwool, are also being used now on a number of bouvardia crops in Holland.

Cuttings are planted out to give a density of 12 to 16 plants/sq m of glasshouse. Planting must be done carefully, and the depth of planting judged so that the top of the root ball is level with the soil surface. The root system of Bouvardia is fine and delicate, and it is not enough to just push the cuttings into the bed as with chrysanthemums.

Support

After planting a light watering in should be given. The growth of this crop is open and soft, and adequate support must be provided. Four layers of netting are recommended, the lower three of 20cm mesh, while the top layer can be wider to make harvesting easier.

After a flush, all the layers of supports are returned to the ground level to be raised again as growth re-commences.

Watering and temperatures

Watering during the summer months should be related to the growth of the crop, and can be freely applied. From September onwards the quantities applied should be greatly reduced until on most soils hardly any water should be given between the beginning of November and mid-February.

At some time during this winter period a resting stage of about six weeks should be given. This involves reducing the temperature to 8-12C and drying the crop right back.

At the end of this resting period the crop is cut back to about 20cm above soil level and the temperatures raised to 15C by night and rather higher during the day.

As soon as the buds show signs of active growth the crop can be given water, and at this time a fungicidal spray will reduce the risk of foot rot developing in the warmer, moist conditions.

When the crop is in active growth, the night temperature should be around 16-17C, although 18C is better for the first few weeks after planting. Day temperatures can be allowed to run up as high as 23C according to the weather, and ventilation applied if temperatures exceed this level.

Light shading may be needed in the summer to reduce plant stress. Sudden climatic changes should be avoided, because they encourage leaf scorch, and occasional damping down of the crop should be given in low humidity conditions, particularly when the ventilators are first opened.

Stopping

A good December flush is encouraged by repeating the stopping operation after the summer flush has been taken. Pink selections should be taken down to three pairs of leaves at the beginning of August, and red and white selections by the middle of the month. A light application of a nitrogenous fertiliser encourages strong regrowth after summer stopping.

Bouvardia make a great deal of sideshoot growth. Any shoots which grow out close to the top of the stem and extend above the flower head, must be removed before marketing. They can be removed before harvesting but this operation must not be carried out too soon, because re-growth may make a second de-shooting necessary.

It is probably better to remove these shoots in the packing shed because, apart from being a less labour-consuming operation, it is then possible to leave on the stem any shoots which do not reach the flower head, so giving a fuller appearance to the bunch.

Bouvardia has a limited photoperiodic response. Work at Aalsmeer in Holland has shown that flower induction is quicker and more uniform if the crop has two or three weeks of short days after planting. Attempts to delay flowering time by using lights to extend the daylength for a period of time after planting have given variable and generally unsuccessful results however.

Carbon dioxide enrichment in the spring can shorten the growing time to the first flush and give stronger stems, although these are also noticeably shorter.

HARVESTING

Bouvardia crops are kept in production for between two and four years, and in a full year it is possible to take three or even four flushes. In a typical crop the first flush after the winter rest comes from the end of April to the beginning of June, and the second in July and August.

To achieve a worthwhile winter flush requires stopping the plants at the end of the summer cut and if this is done a third flush is taken during November or December.

Yields in a full year can be between six and eight stems per plant from each flush, but the first year flush is likely to be only about four stems.

The stems are usually cut when the first two or three flowers are open although white varieties should be harvested a little earlier than this, as they are more susceptible to damage in transit. Harvesting can be carried out by breaking off the stem, or by using a knife or secateurs.

Bouvardia is sensitive to water loss from the cut stems, and these should always be placed into water within 10 minutes of harvesting.

They are bunched in separate colours, with 10 stems per bunch, and then bundled into groups of five bunches.

If the stems droop they seldom recover satisfactorily, although the use of a flower preservative material at all stages of the marketing chain helps to get the best from the blooms. Work carried out in Holland on maximising vase life has found that different flower preservative materials have different effects on vase life and bud opening, but that all materials are an improvement on clear water.

Including a wetting agent in the treatment is particularly valuable, as it reduces the risk of air blocks in the cut stems, one of the main causes of vase life reduction.

Flower conditioning before marketing was also found to be very important, and the best results were obtained by holding the stems overnight in a cold store at 2 - 5C. Bouvardia should never be marketed directly after harvesting.

PESTS AND DISEASES

Both aphids and whitefly can become a serious pest on Bouvardia, and insecticide applications should continue at regular intervals. The foliage should be dry at the time of each application which should be directed to the under surface of the leaves, and not aimed at developing blooms, as these are easily scorched.

Integrated pest control, using a combination of biological control agents and chemicals, has been used successfully in Germany on bouvardia.

The only common aerial disease of bouvardia is botrytis. As with other crops the first line of defence should be cultural; keeping the foliage clean, well supported and dry and reducing humidity as far as possible by maintaining good air movement through the crop and ventilating as freely as circumstances permit. A number of fungicides are suitable for botrytis control.

Stem and root diseases of bouvardia are caused by pythium and rhizoctonia. Good crop hygiene and soil sterilisation go a long way towards preventing the establishment of either of these soil-borne fungi.

Cucumber mosaic virus has been identified in bouvardia. This causes a colour-break in the blooms, particularly in the red cultivar as pale flecks. Control in chemical terms is not possible, although the spreading of the virus within the crop can be greatly reduced by maintaining good aphid control, since this is the main transmitting agent, and by pulling up obviously affected plants.

Careful selection of mother plants is important, and they should ideally be virus-indexed against tobacco plants before the production of cuttings begins.

5 Campanula

Biennial, plant December to flower May

Although many Campanula species are not suitable for cut flower production there is one group, Campanula persicifolia, which is now quite often used for this purpose. These are most commonly grown outdoors for summer flowering, but some are grown under glass, which can advance flowering by two or three weeks and so command the best market prices.

The only types of campanula under glass are all selections of Campanula persicifolia. Alba is white, Coerulea is blue and Telham Beauty has large, pale blue flowers. These varieties will flower outdoors in June and for culture under protection to be economic it is necessary to bring the crop into flower in May.

Selections of two other species, Campanula medium and Campanula glomerata, have been trialled for early spring cut flower production under moveable plastic tunnels in both Holland and Germany. The crop is started outdoors in September and covered from December onwards. This will be successful only if low temperatures occur in October and November. If the autumn is mild yields are low and flowering is late.

PROPAGATION

Campanula is grown from seed, and is treated as a biennial when it is grown for cut flowers. The seed is very fine, and is best sown in trays in a suitable seed-raising compost, which should itself have a fine texture.

After sowing, the seed should be thinly covered and carefully firmed. After covering with glass or plastic the trays should be kept in the glasshouse until emergence, after which they should be damped over occasionally in sunny weather to avoid leaf scorch.

Seed can be sown at any time between March and June, although for glasshouse culture it is better not to sow before the middle of May. Earlier sowings do not come into flowering quicker, they just make more foliage, and this increases the risk of botrytis developing during damp weather.

Sowings after the beginning of June may fail to make sufficient growth by the winter if growing conditions are poor during the autumn.

CROP CULTURE
When the seedlings are big enough to handle they can be pricked off into trays or Into the open ground, although it is possible to omit this stage if the seed has been sown thinly enough. In July or August the plants should be transplanted outdoors at a density of 10 to 15 plants/sq m.

Campanulas are very sensitive to root damage, and so should be moved carefully with a ball of compost still attached to the roots.

For outdoor production the plants are then grown through the winter to flower without being moved further, while for flowering under glass the plants should be moved inside, again with a good root ball, In December. For glasshouse production it is important to build up a hard plant without excessive vigour, because botrytis infection can otherwisecause serious losses.

Soil analysis before the final transplanting will show whether fertilisers are needed and it is usual to apply some sulphate of potash to encourage rather hard growth.

Water should be applied in sufficient quantities to maintain steady growth. but not excessively.

It is not necessary to heat the crop during the winter, and it is doubtful whether it would be economic to do so, although the ability to heat in still, damp weather if botrytis threatens may be an advantage.

Very little water is needed through the coldest months, and ventilation should be freely applied whenever possible. A single layer of netting should be used as a crop support because the growth of the plants tends to be rather soft under glass, and the flower stems will not remain straight without some support.

HARVESTING
Campanula persicifolia should be harvested when the first buds on the stem are showing colour, but before they open. The development of the flowers can be very rapid in warm weather, and if one or more flowers are open when the stem is picked the blooms will often be too advanced by the time they reach market.

Campanula is usually bunched in tens, although a proportion of the stems will be thin and weak and it is advisable to bunch these in larger numbers to give a bunch of uniform bulk.

PESTS AND DISEASES
Botrytis grey mould is the most common disease problem, and care must be taken to water as little as possible and to ventilate freely in dull weather in the winter and early spring.

Rust

The orange spots of rust are often seen on Campanula persicifolia and this too spreads in damp conditions.

Wet sprays of a suitable fungicide will give some control while precautionary applications of dust can be put on to the crop at seven- to 10-day intervals before rust is seen. Badly affected plants should be removed immediately, and plants more lightly infected should be cleared as soon as the flower stems have been harvested.

Sclerotinia

Sclerotinia rot sometimes develops in dense plantings. It appears first as a white mould around the base of the plant, and later shows the characteristic grey or black sclerotia. Good air movement and a dry atmosphere limit the spread of this disease, while a fungicidal soil drench will provide a measure of control.

Infected plants should be removed, together with the soil in their immediate vicinity. If a further crop is to be grown in the same soil it should be sterilised in some way.

Aphids and mites

The usual pest problems of most cut flower crops can develop on Campanula, particularly aphids and red spider mite.

6 Delphiniums

Annual, sow March - May to flower end May - June

Although delphiniums have a place in the cut flower market, and make an attractive long-lasting inflorescence, they are more commonly grown outdoors. Although there is the risk that a crop grown under glass may produce excessively soft foliage and rather pale blooms, careful culture will give an acceptable product with a market premium for earliness.

The market interest in delphiniums has increased considerably in the last few years, particularly now that the crop has found a role of some importance as dried blooms.

Two species are grown commercially for cut flowers. Both are annuals, and are available in a range of attractive colours. Delphinium consolida has a freely branching habit, and in a well-grown crop will produce some marketable side stems. Delphinium ajacis, also known as Larkspur, produces only a single stem under most conditions, but flowers about two weeks earlier. Both species grow to a height of about 120-150cm outdoors, but only Delphinium ajacis is in demand for dried flower production.

Mixed strains of doubles are usually offered for Delphinium ajacis, while Delphinium consolida is available in a range of individual colours, including picotees. Not all varieties on offer are suitable for glasshouse production however. Delphinium consolida Blue Cloud is a bright blue small-flowered type which has a growth habit similar to gypsophila.

PROPAGATION

Seed of either type is sown between mid-March and mid-May for production under glass or in tunnels. The direct seeding rate should be around 1g/sq m.

Germination is rapid, provided the soil remains uniformly moist until emergence is complete. Germination at around 20C will give the quickest and most uniform emergence. It should not be necessary to thin out the plants in the row unless over-seeding has produced occasional clumps of plants.

CROP CULTURE

For culture under glass it is important to keep the growth as hard as possible by applying full ventilation whenever conditions permit and by avoiding excessive watering. Otherwise the crop should be allowed to grow quite freely for maximum quality.

Fertiliser levels should be adequate for growth and a base dressing will often not be needed under glass where the previous crop has been regularly fed.

One or two liquid feeds or top dressings with a general granular feed should be applied.

Some form of crop supports will be needed under glass, and a single layer of wide-gauge mesh is suitable.

HARVESTING

The crop will be ready to harvest under glass from mid-May to the end of June, depending on the sowing date and the species. Delphinium ajacis flowers about two weeks earlier than Delphinium consolida.

Delphiniums are ready to cut when about half of the flowers on the stem are open or opening if the blooms are to be used fresh. For dried flower work at least 90% of the flowers should be open when the stems are cut. It should be possible to achieve a yield of around four bunches/sq m glasshouse floor area.

PESTS AND DISEASES

One specific disease attacks delphiniums, crown rot caused by the fungus sclero-tinia. This causes a rotting of the base of the stem, followed by wilting of the plant. If the root system is examined it is usually possible to see yellow or brown sclerotia on the roots. Prevention or control of crown rot takes the form of a soil drench with an appropriate fungicide.

Delphiniums are also susceptible to mildew, which can be controlled by the use of wet sprays of a suitable fungicide.

7 Eustoma

Annual, plant March - April to flower June - July

Eustoma grandiflorum, which originated in the southern USA, started its career as a cut flower crop more than 15 years ago under its alternative name of Lisianthus. Since that time there has been a vast improvement in the range of varieties available and better ones are being introduced all the time. Eustoma is usually grown as a single-flush annual crop, although it is sometimes kept in place for a smaller second flush, or even for a second year.

Eustoma is a daylength neutral species and it can be brought into flower at any time of the year, but supplementary lighting is needed for successful winter production so it is generally grown for spring or summer flowering.

Eustoma is very susceptible to air-borne fungal diseases and is best grown in structures with plenty of ventilation and pipe heating.

Varieties

A wide range of colours is already available, including some good bicolours and picotees but more and better varieties are appearing all the time. The taller varieties, up to 90cm, are best used for summer flowering, and the medium height sorts, around 70cm tall, for spring or autumn cropping.

The Yodel series was widely grown a few years ago but this has recently been superseded by others, such as the Fuji range. These come in several good colours and have a more upright growth habit. They are of medium height and are best used either for planting early in the year or for May planting to flower in the autumn.

The Kyoto range is taller and better for summer flowering from plantings in mid-March onwards.

Some doubles are also available now including the medium height Dream range. These still tend to be a bit variable but better and more uniform doubles are expected to make their appearance soon.

Plants should be put in in late January if lighting is not available otherwise they will flower too quickly on short stems, especially if low temperatures are used. End of January plantings, from a September sowing, will come into flower from late May onwards.

The latest planting should be made around the middle of June, to flower in late October. The latest plantings will progressively produce poorer quality blooms.

PROPAGATION

Most Eustoma growers either produce or buy in seedlings, which are best grown in extra deep plugs to allow for the deep root system of this crop. Pelleted seed is usually sown and seedlings emerge in about two weeks if the temperature is kept around the optimum 22–24C.

The compost should be treated with a preventative fungicide before sowings, because the seedlings are very susceptible to damping off fungi.

Early plant growth is slow and plants will take three to four months from sowing before they are ready to be planted out. The earliest plantings will therefore need to be sown in September of the previous year. A minimum night temperature of 16–18C should be maintained through the propagation period, rising further on bright days.

If temperatures are too low the plants will tend to bolt and flower too early on short stems. If 24-hour temperatures are allowed to exceed about 24C, even for only a few days, the plants will tend to rosette rather than extend upwards and stem length will be greatly reduced. Some older varieties are more susceptible to rosetting than recent hybrids.

ESTABLISHMENT

Eustoma has a long root system and it is important to cultivate the soil down to at least 75cm. Fertiliser should be incorporated only if the nutrient status of the soil is very low, because the plants are very sensitive to high salt levels.

Excessive nitrogen levels in particular can encourage vegetative basal growth at the expense of flower quality. If the soil conductivity is high, leaching should be carried out before planting to ensure good plant vigour.

The pH of the soil or growing medium is important. A pH of around 6.4 is ideal. If the pH is below about 5.7 the plants take up large amounts of zinc and this causes leaf chlorosis and tip scorch, eventually stunting the growth of the plants. There is evidence that high pH can be a problem, too, reducing flower colour intensity.

Plant density

Plant density should be between 40 to 50/sq m of glasshouse area, with the closer spacing used for the shorter varieties. Higher densities give some increase in yield but at the expense of quality and vice versa.

A single layer of 12.5cm net should be put down at planting time to support the crop as it approaches flowering.

CROP CULTURE

Once the young plants are established the crop should be kept in active growth by maintaining a minimum 24-hour air temperature of around 17C. If this is not achieved the development of the crop can be very slow. Night temperatures above 18C should be avoided, particularly in the later stages, to prevent poor flower quality.

It is best to take only a single stem per plant to ensure top quality, although pinching the plant back to three to five buds about three weeks after planting has been tried experimentally but is not likely to be worthwhile economically.

Time from sowing to flowering of an unpinched crop is very dependent on sowing date. It can be as short as six months from a February-March sowing – that is, about two months from planting to flowering – or as long as 10 months from an over-wintered September sowing.

The surface of the soil should be kept as dry as possible to keep fungal infection at bay. This is best done by using low level irrigation rather than applying water over the crop. This enables plenty of water to be supplied to the full depth of the root system without generating high humidities within the foliage. Watering can be gradually eased off as the first buds become visible.

HARVESTING

The first flower on each stem can sometimes open well ahead of the remainder and it is often worth pinching this off to allow a more balanced spray to develop. The stem should be harvested when two or three flowers are fully open.

It is not practicable to pull up the whole plant when harvesting, even when the crop is being cleared, because the root system is too strong. Instead, cut the stem or break it off close to the ground.

Eustoma does not travel well and marketing in aqua-packs is usually necessary. If the crop is handled carefully it should be possible to get a vase life of about three weeks. Italian research has demonstrated that vase life and the intensity of colour of the later opening blooms can both be improved by treating the cut stems with a solution containing a bactericide and sugar.

PESTS AND DISEASES

Damping off can be a big problem during propagation and establishment and preventative fungicidal treatment is a must.

Downy mildew, caused by the fungus Perenospora chlorae, can quickly spoil the foliage in the later stages of growth and this must be recognised early and checked with fungicidal wet sprays before it gets out of hand. Downy mildew is seen as small light spots on the upper leaf surface, with matching areas of purple mould underneath the leaf.

Botrytis and penicillium are both common problems, too, although the latter is usually secondary.

A number of viruses have been identified in eustoma, including yellow bean mosaic, tomato mosaic and cucumber mosaic. All of these are spread by aphids.

8 Gerbera

Perennial, plant February - March to flower May onwards

The market for cut flower gerberas is still expanding in the UK, but it has a long way to go to catch up with the situation in Holland, where gerberas are ranked seven in the list of the top 10 cut flowers, and set to rise as better varieties and new types attract more growers and more consumers.

Profitable gerbera production is particularly dependent on good quality facilities. Good winter light is essential, and accurate climate control is a must to keep the crop healthy and growing well. Good crops can be grown in the soil, but the best growers in Holland now use rockwool.

Production levels in rockwool are generally 30 to 50% higher than in soil and the additional investment cost of rockwool is quickly recovered.

Varieties

Gerbera varieties are classified as single or double, although there are also many semi-double types. The singles produce more blooms per square metre, but the doubles fetch a market premium, so the overall economics of both are much the same. Traditional gerbera varieties, or standards, have a flower diameter of 9cm upwards, and typically yield 100 to 150 stems/sq m in the soil, or around 200 stems in rockwool. The most widely grown standards at present include Beauty, Estelle, Rosamunda, King and Tamara.

Many new varieties appear every year, and among the recently introduced standard types are Fireball and Ornella (orange), Yellowspot and Gold Rush (yellow), Cathy (pink), and the yellow/orange double Sax.

Recent introductions will usually have a quality edge over older types, because all the major plant breeders now operate a Reference Test scheme in which a number of quality factors are taken into account before a potential new variety is released. Vase life, recovery after transport and susceptibility to handling damage are all assessed.

A range of varieties with rather smaller blooms, 8 to 9cm diameter, is also available. These have a limited appeal but a smaller group still, the mini types, represent more than a third of all Dutch gerbera production. These have a flower diameter of 6 to 8cm, and the can yield 350 or more stems/sq m when grown in rockwool. The most popular include Ballet, Salsa and Sirtaki, but there are dozens of new introductions to consider too. These include Illusion (yellow), Joy (orange), Pink Joy, Prelude (lilac) and Tattoo, cream with a red centre.

One step down again from the minis is the micro series, which includes a number of recent additions in the Picolini range. Micro gerberas have flower diameters between 4 and 6cm, and have the highest yields of all – up to 450 stems/sq m in rockwool.

Crop terms

Gerberas are usually kept in production for two years or more if the crop is kept in good condition and disease-free. The optimum planting date is around March because although early production is limited, establishment of the crop is good and total yield is high. If the crop is to be grown only for 18 months, then July is a better starting date because winter production will be better.

Gerberas are occasionally treated as short-term crops, planting early in the year, and clearing in December. In this case it is important to plant as early as possible and certainly by the middle of February. The planting date has a very big influence on early yield and any delay reduces the output considerably. For the same reason it is important to encourage rapid establishment and to avoid any checks to growth.

PROPAGATION

Raising gerbera plants by vegetative means is normally carried out by specialist propagators, although it is possible for growers to maintain their own mother plant stocks. To provide good material for shoot production the mother plants have to be grown at a high temperature, around 25-30C.

As shoots develop they are removed from the parent plant and rooted under mist or in a polythene tent, again using a peat-based compost. Rooting is quicker and more uniform if it is possible to give bottom heat to maintain 25C.

Many gerbera varieties are now produced by micropropagation. Although these will be more expensive than traditionally propagated plants they repay the cost by coming into flower more quickly – usually within two to three months after planting. First year production can therefore be high, up to 40 blooms/plant, depending on the variety and the substrate.

ESTABLISHMENT – SOIL

Gerbera plants should be planted without delay after delivery, and if they are to establish successfully they should be put into a warm substrate. For soil-grown crops, if soil warming is available it should be turned on about a week before the plants arrive, and run up over this period to a final soil temperature of about 20C.

The soil should be moist but not wet for planting, and a light watering in should be given, avoiding getting the crown of the plants wet. Root zone and air temperatures should be held in the range 20-22C while the plants are establishing, and the humidity should be kept up to 80-90% to maintain maximum early growth.

Watering rates should be quite low at first, but will need to increase considerably as the plants start to grow away when water consumption rises rapidly.

Gerberas are very susceptible to fungal and bacterial rots of the crown, and these rots can cause considerable plant losses. It is essential that the plants are set out in such a way that the crown is clear of the surface, and unlikely to be regularly wetted during watering. For direct planting into soil, this means that the plants should be set out a little above the finished soil surface.

A more reliable planting method is to put the plants into large pots or buckets, with a good size hole underneath to allow rooting through into the bed. Even here, deep planting should be avoided, and a suitable irrigation system is necessary.

Gerbera crops are most usually kept in for about two years and for this reason careful soil sterilisation and preparation is particularly important. The soil should be sterilised before planting.

Soil conditioning

If the soil structure is poor, a soil conditioning material such as peat should be incorporated in sufficient proportion to make a good rooting medium, but not in excessive amounts, as this can lead to problems with watering later on.

The soil should be subjected to chemical analysis before planting, and any corrective measures which may be needed taken at this time. If the salt level is at all high, a good volume of water should be applied to leach out the excess.

Any nutritional short-fall should be made good at this stage by the use of base fertilisers, although overall levels do not need to be high, particularly if a regular liquid feeding programme is to be employed.

Plant establishment may be slow if the nutrient status of the soil is high, especially in any drier areas of the house. Lime should only be applied if the soil is acid, aiming for a pH in the range 6.0 to 6.5.

Planting density

The planting density should be related to the length of time the crop is to remain in production, and also to the vigour of the variety. For two-year crops it is usual to plant up at between five and seven plants/gross sq m depending on the vigour of the cultivar. For short term crops the plant density can be rather greater.

Gerberas do not need crop supports.

ESTABLISHMENT – ROCKWOOL

For production in rockwool, slabs 15cm wide and 10cm deep are generally used. These are arranged in double rows to give a plant spacing of 6.5 to 8/sq m of glasshouse. A pipe loop beneath the rows should be installed for substrate warming, which is very beneficial for gerberas.

Plants are raised either in rockwool cubes or in pots of rockwool flock, and these should not be put out on to the slabs until a good white root mat has formed on the under side. Placing out too early will lead to irregular establishment and growth.

The rockwool slabs should not be slit for drainage at first. A high water table should be established at planting time, and allowed to drop in stages as the root system follows it downwards.

CROP CULTURE

Gerberas need a lot of water when they are in active growth, but because of the risk of fungal rots the method of application is important. Overhead irrigation should be avoided and watering through individual drip nozzles pegged some way from the centre of the plant is best for both soil and rockwool crops.

It is essential that the crown of the plant is kept dry, especially at night, and so watering should be carried out early in the day if possible.

Overhead damping down to maintain humidity or provide evaporative cooling should be carried out with a minimal volume of water applied as a fine mist. Watering rates for soil-grown crops should be reduced as winter approaches, although the soil should remain moist if the crop is being kept in active growth. An occasional check with a soil auger will show whether the irrigation schedule is suitable.

Nutrition

Gerberas do not have a high nutritional requirement, and cultural problems soon develop if high salt levels are allowed to build up in the soil. A good level of phosphate is necessary to encourage a strong root system, and so the base fertiliser application should include a suitable amount of superphosphate or triple superphosphate. Nitrate and potash levels should be maintained by continuous liquid feeding with a solution giving 100 ppm of nitrate and 200 ppm of potash.

Alternatively feeds at twice this strength can be alternated with clear water, but in this case there is a greater risk of root scorch if the feed is applied to dry soil. In the early summer a higher proportion of nitrogen may be necessary to encourage more plant vigour, and a liquid feed based on 150 ppm each of nitrate and potash may be used at this time.

Occasional chemical analysis of the soil should be carried out to verify the feeding programme, and this is particularly important at the start of the second year of production. Gerberas are inclined to develop symptoms of trace element deficiency from time to time. These may be caused either by a lack of trace elements in the substrate or by the failure of the plant to take them up. In either case, a light application of chelated trace elements should be included in the liquid feed once every few weeks, and more frequently if symptoms are observed.

Iron deficiency symptoms are commonly seen, with the younger leaves showing a butter yellow discolouration showing up against the green veins and these symptoms can quickly be reversed by an application of iron chelate in the liquid feed, either over the whole crop or to a specific area if the problem is localised.

Deleafing

The amount of foliage which develops on the crop during the first year is not usually enough to require de-leafing, but for two-year crops this operation should be carried out. During the winter, about nine to 10 months after planting, a proportion of the older leaves should be cut out to re-establish an open plant.

A sharp knife should be used and care taken to avoid damaging the crown or leaving snags which could become a site for botrytis and other infections. During the second year of growth de-leafing should be carried out occasionally to thin out excessively dense foliage.

If this is done regularly, and without removing too many leaves on any one occasion, it can improve flower quality and reduce the risk of disease establishment.

Carbon dioxide

Carbondioxide is now widely used on gerberas during the heating season. An enrichment level of 500-600 vpm has been shown to give a worthwhile increase in both yield and flower quality.

Lighting

Assimilation lighting has been tried experimentally on rockwool crops in Belgium, using 16 hour-days of 10 watts/sq m at crop height. Lighting gave some yield increases, but whether lighting is economic has not yet been established.

CULTURE IN ROCKWOOL

An irrigation frequency of 4 to 8 times per day is needed for gerberas, allowing enough run-off at each watering to keep the nutrient solution balanced. An initial feed strength of 2.0 mS/cm is suitable, rising to 2.5 mS as the rate of growth increases in the spring. In the summer it may be necessary to drop back to 2.0 mS to prevent the conductivity of the slabs rising too high.

At 2.0 mS the input solution should contain around 180 ppm NO3-N, 45 ppm P, 250 ppm K, 160 ppm Ca and 25 ppm Mg. A frequent check should правильно be made on the pH of the slab solution, because this can be greatly influenced by plant growth rate.

HARVESTING

Gerberas come into production quite quickly, and the first marketable blooms can generally be cut from crops started from cuttings within about two months after planting, depending on temperature, substrate and variety. Crops from seed may take up to three months from planting out.

The biggest problem with gerberas is to produce a bloom which has a long and reliable vase life. Incorrect handling techniques result in flowers which fail to take up water successfully and which droop irrecoverably.

One of the most important factors is to harvest the blooms at the proper stage. Immature blooms tend to take up water less well.

The stage of maturity is determined by looking at the rings of stamens within the petals. Two or three of these rings should be visible when the flower is harvested. The correct stage is quite easily recognised with experience although it is not so easy to identify in the case of double or semi-double varieties.

Flowers should be harvested by pulling away the crown and they should be carried into the packing shed in water rather than dry.

Post-harvest treatment

In the shed the blooms should be suspended in water by passing them through a frame of wire or plastic mesh. If the blooms then go through a period of softness before the stems return to their rigid state, the stems do not become bent.

The water in which gerberas are held should always contain a preservative, as this has a considerable effect on vase life of the blooms. It is also worthwhile marketing the flowers complete with a sachet of flower preservative.

The preparation, grading and presentation of gerberas for the market will depend on local requirements. The blooms are quite difficult to pack for transport. Clear plastic cups are still available into which the blooms are pulled, and which protect the heads by holding them in a semi-closed state. In Holland these have now been largely superseded by moulded card inserts which hold the blooms in place.

PESTS AND DISEASES

Three wilt diseases of some importance can attack gerberas – verticillium, fusarium and phytophthora. In each case the rate of spread in relation to soil temperature is different, although all are more likely to become established in poor soil conditions. It is essential that the structure and drainage of the soil and sub-soil are corrected before planting, especially prior to planting crops which are to be grown on for two years.

Planting in individual containers with basal holes through which the roots can eventually emerge has the advantage that diseased plants can be removed with less opportunity for the fungus to spread to adjacent plants.

Soil-grown plants should be set with their crown clear of the surface, because the risk of disease becoming established is greater if the crown remains wet after watering. Once the plants are growing away watering must be carefully regulated to ensure that the soil never becomes waterlogged or excessively dry.

Roots growing freely in an open soil with a good balance between aeration and water supply and without high salt levels are much less likely to pick up wilt infection than those which are stunted, damaged or scorched.

Verticillium and fusarium wilts are superficially similar, although verticillium tends to affect individual leaves at first, while fusarium causes a more general plant collapse.

It is not essential to identify which of the two diseases is responsible for plant losses, because in each case the chemical control measures are the same, but the rate of spread in relation to temperature will usually suggest which of the two wilts is present.

Verticillium spreads only slowly from plant to plant, and is essentially a low temperature disease. Fusarium can spread very much more quickly and is a much greater problem in the summer when soil temperatures are high. In either case infected plants should be carefully removed as soon as the cause of collapse is ascertained, and the soil drenched with a fungicide.

If fusarium is identified, steps should be taken to reduce the soil temperature by shading the crop and damping over frequently in sun.

Phytophthora cryptogea, or foot rot, is probably the most serious wilt disease of soil-grown gerberas in Holland, where it proves very difficult to eradicate once it has become established.

Like fusarium and verticillium, it can be greatly reduced by steam sterilisation between crops, but even then it is quite likely to re-appear in the following crop. It seems to spread faster under low temperature conditions, and keeping the soil temperature above 20C reduces the risk of phytophthora becoming established.

Other diseases

A number of general root rot fungi also attack gerberas, and their control is important not only to maintain the vigour of the crop, but also because roots damaged in this way are more likely to be attacked by the wilt fungi. Young plants may become infected by pythium. Older plants are more likely to be attacked by rhizoctonia.

The foliage and flowers of gerberas can be seriously affected by the characteristic grey mould of botrytis, particularly in the autumn and winter when a damp climate persists. As well as causing leaf rot, botrytis will cause spotting of the petals which can quickly render the blooms unmarketable. In conditions of dull weather and high atmospheric humidity every effort should be made to keep the foliage dry.

Maximum ventilation should be given whenever possible, and heat applied to provide air movement through the crop. Overhead spraying should be stopped, and the crop watered as seldom as possible. Dead or damaged leaves or plants should be cleaned out of the crop regularly.

Mildew sometimes attacks gerbera foliage, forming a white powdery deposit on the leaves. Like botrytis, this disease thrives in damp conditions and a drier climate in the glasshouse will go a long way towards limiting its spread.

Insect pests

A number of insects and other pests will attack gerberas, of which the most persistent is usually whitefly. They can cause serious damage to the foliage and are difficult to eradicate once they become well established. It is therefore important to apply a suitable insecticide as soon as an outbreak is noticed.

Gerberas can sometimes be quite badly scorched by certain insecticides and acaricides, and any material being employed for the first time should be trialled on a small area before large-scale application, and the usual common-sense rules of when and how to apply pesticides should be followed conscientiously.

9 Gypsophila

Cut-flower gypsophila can be grown either from the annual Gypsophila elegans or from the perennial Gypsophila paniculata

The propagation, culture and management of the annual and perennial types of gypshophila are different and distinct.

GYPSOPHILA ELEGANS

Annual, sow February onwards to flower from May

Gypsophila elegans is an annual crop, grown from seed. The wild form has small white flowers but an extensive breeding programme has resulted in a range of commercial varieties suitable for cut-flower production under glass or outdoors.

The white variety Roem Van Rijnsburg is still widely grown, but there are improved white varieties like Snow Fountain available now. These have a stronger more erect growth habit. A range of pink flowered varieties is also available.

PROPAGATION

Gypsophila elegans needs a light, well-drained soil for best results. The nutrient levels in the soil must be low, because if the crop grows too strongly the growth becomes too weak and flower quality suffers. For this reason it is usual to apply no base fertiliser before sowing under glass, and it is often necessary to leach excess nutrients from the soil.

Soil sterilisation should be carried out annually to maintain a reasonably weed-free situation, although few specific soil-borne pests or diseases are known to be a problem on gypsophila.

The crop is sown by broadcasting the seed, mixed with a greater volume of sand to help achieve a good distribution. It is not necessary to cover the seed, but the soil should be well watered before sowing and then sprayed over regularly to maintain a good moisture level until the young plants have emerged and are well established.

Germination is rapid and emergence will be noticed in as few as four days under the temperature conditions which apply to late spring sowings. Even the earliest sowings under glass should have emerged within about 10 days if the soil has been kept moist at all times.

CROP CULTURE

Annual gypsophila can be sown from late February onwards under glass, and between early April and the beginning of August outdoors. The time from sowing to harvesting is proportional to the temperature.

The earliest sowings in cold glass will be ready to cut in eight to 10 weeks, so that the first stems will appear on the market around the end of April. Later sowings are increasingly quicker-growing, and gypsophila sown in April is in flower after only five or six weeks.

It is possible to make sequential sowings under glass at two-week intervals to crop throughout the summer. In Holland it is usual to sow such crops at a lower seeding rate. The lower density of crop improves the quality of the summer cuts, although there is a reduction in yield per unit area. After the end of June, outdoor sowings, which mature in eight to 10 weeks, appear on the market and quality is often better than glasshouse grown as growth is less soft.

Crop supports are not needed for higher seeding rates asplants are self-supporting. But the lower plant density of summer crops a single layer of 20cm wire mesh is needed, laid out over the beds after sowing and raised as the crop grows.

Temperature regimes

The temperature requirements of gypsophila should be related to sowing date, aiming to keep the crop hard without slowing down the growth unnecessarily.

Crops growing in March should be kept at a maximum of about 13C, while in April and May this can safely be raised to 15-16C. The problem in the summer is to run temperatures low enough to produce acceptable growth.

Little is known about the plant's response to the lower light levels which follow from shading the crop, but it would certainly be an advantage to apply shading in July and August if temperatures would otherwise often exceed 20C.

Watering and feeding

The application of water to the crop should gradually be reduced as the flower buds develop, until no water at all is given from just before the start of picking. This reduces the risk of botrytis infection of the flowers, and also helps to maintain a strong flower stem.

If the early vigour of the crop is too great, and there is a risk of weakening the flower stems excessively, the watering rate should be cut down earlier than would otherwise be the case. It is not usual to apply any fertiliser during the course of the growing period of gypsophila because of the adverse effect this has on stem strength.

HARVESTING

Harvesting of annual gypsophila is carried out by pulling up the whole plant when the flower stem reaches the correct stage of maturity, when the majority of the flowers are open. The roots are cut off after bunching, and it is important that the cut stems are quickly put into very clean water with a flower conditioner.

PESTS AND DISEASES

Botrytis is the only disease which regularly causes problems on annual gypsophila. It frequently attacks the young seedlings soon after emergence and can infect the flowers and flower stem. Early attacks can be prevented by dusting the surface of the bed immediately after sowing and repeating this after 10 days. Flower stem infection can be avoided if the crop is kept dry and well ventilated at this stage. A little pipe heat at night, if available, together with some ventilation will help limit the spread of botrytis if an attack occurs.

Aphid and caterpillars may need to be controlled

GYPSOPHILA PANICULATA

Perennial, plant March - April to flower May - June and September

Perennial gypsophila, like Gypsophila elegans, thrives in dry conditions. The wild form, Gypsophila paniculata, is not very suitable for commercial growing. It produces 1m tall, slender sprays of small, single white flower.

However there are a number of commercial varieties including: G. paniculata Plena (a double white, with smallish flowers and a stem length really too short for reliable cut-flower production); G. paniculata Bristol Fairy (large double white flowers with stems up to 4ft); G. paniculata Bristol Fairy perfecta (a selection from Bristol Fairy which has larger flowers of greater bulk, but the stem length is rather less and the blooms mature later); G. paniculata Flamingo (a single pink variety, with a stem length of 1m or more).

A number of new Israeli varieties – Romano 4 and Ehrlei in particular - are of interest because they will accept shorter daylength than standard varieties. Both will also bloom under daylength and temperature conditions lower than those which would be suitable for Bristol Fairy.

PROPAGATION

Unlike annual gypsophila, these perennial varieties are not raised from seed for commercial production. because a high proportion of single flowered plants develop from seed of the popular double varieties lowering their value as cut-flowers.

Top quality planting material of perennial gypsophila is mainly produced by micro-propagation. The young plants need to be handled carefully during establishment, but repay this attention by growing away rapidly and by producing higher early yields.

ESTABLISHMENT

Like annual gypsophila the perennial varieties need an open, free-draining soil. Grafted plants in particular seem to grow best in a coarse, gravelly substrate with plenty of air spaces between the soil particles. The plants do not grow well in the winter unless the soil is quite dry, and it is not a suitable crop for glasshouse situations where there is a high water table.

Similarly Gypsophila paniculata does not establish well outdoors unless winter rainfall is low. If the crop is being grown as a perennial it is very important to cultivate deeply to ensure a deep root run for plants in their second year.

For culture under glass, plants are usually received in early spring, although it is possible to start as early as January or February. Traditionally propagated plants in the first season need early establishment, and the crop will be light unless the plants are in by about the end of May. Micropropagated plants are often planted in May, but these establish and grow away more quickly to bloom well in their first season. (Colombian work suggests that storing rooted cuttings for four weeks at 0C/80% RH pre-planting advances flowering by two weeks, but this is untested in Europe.)

CROP CULTURE

For the first few weeks after planting the crop should be kept cool, down to 8-12C according to prevailing light levels. This is because the extent to which the plants will branch – and the number of stems which will eventually be cut – is determined by temperature at this stage.

Once the crop is established, and when second-year crops start into growth in the early spring, there can be a gradual rise in temperature. Higher than normal temperatures can be used to advance flowering a little, while low temperatures will do no harm to the crop other than to delay flowering.

As a rule the temperatures should be around 15-16C in February and March, gradually rising towards 18C by early April. Day temperatures can safely be allowed to rise to 25C in bright sun.

Long days and a good overall light intensity are necessary for good bloom production. Forcing in poor light conditions may lead to a proportion of blind buds, which reduce yield and flower quality.

The watering regime for Gypsophila paniculata should take into account the crop's preference for rather dry soil conditions at all stages. Any form of irrigation system is suitable, although there is a preference in Holland for drip or trickle installations which supply enough water to the deeper roots without wetting the surface layers of the soil too much.

Because of the susceptibility of the buds to botrytis, no water at all should usually be given once the crop approaches the flowering stage.

Gypsophila has a low nutritional requirement and no feeding is normally necessary for one year crops. Crops grown on for a second or third year may need a low level of general fertiliser application in the spring, although this should be preceded by soil analysis to be sure that it is necessary.

Daylength factors

Israeli techniques on the daylength requirements of Gypsophila paniculata has been adopted by some Dutch growers. Bud initiation and development depends on daylength and varieties differ in their specific requirements.

For a standard variety like Bristol Fairy the optimum daylength for rapid flowering ranges between 14 and 16 hours, depending on mean temperature between 23 and 17C respectively. Some more modern varieties, like Romano 4, have a lower optimum daylength (13-15 hours) and a lower related mean temperature (20-15C).

Under normal temperature regimes, therefore, it seems that artificial illumination given to advance flowering must be based on at least a 15-hour day.

Long days should not be given for the first three or four weeks of growth because the vegetative phase of the plant, - important if a good yield is to be achieved - is dependent on short days (less than 11 hours) and low temperatures (below 10-12C).

Once long-day conditions are applied, they should be maintained for a period of several weeks to develop a full crop. Lighting techniques such as night-break lighting and cyclic lighting can be used.

Cutting back

If a crop of perennial gypsophila is to be retained for a second or third year, it should be cut back to within an inch or two of the ground in the autumn or winter, and kept cold and dry until it is started into growth again in the early spring. The most usual cutting back date is in December, although it is possible to delay until early February.

The later date should be used only if high temperature culture is to follow, because the main flowering period may otherwise overlap with outdoor crops, and consequently fetch lower market returns.

Flowering dates

Because the rate of flower development depends on both temperature and light levels, the time of flowering from autumn-started flushes is greatly affected by the date of establishment. Crops started 10 days later in the autumn will flower at least three weeks later. The opposite effect is seen in spring-started crops, when the flowering date is largely independent of the date of starting into growth.

Perennial gypsophila grown without daylength control will come into production around May or June in its first year, and rather earlier in subsequent years. The bulk of the crop will be taken before outside crops come into full production in July and August, although a second cut of blooms may still be cut as late as October.

HARVESTING

Flower stems of perennial gypsophila are cut close to the ground, rather than being pulled. A proportion of the plants, sometimes up to 10%, will fail to flower. Research in the USA suggests that in some cases this can be aggravated by root damage – either physical or insect-induced – or by growing the crop very wet or very dry.

10 Liatris

Annual, grown from corms planted end January to early February for flowering May and June

L iatris is a crop which is grown commercially from corms and which is gaining steadily in importance as cultural techniques are developed to produce blooms outside the normal summer flowering period. Outside crops come into flower from July to early August. Crops under glass can be manipulated to flower as early as the middle of May or as late as November.

In Holland there is still increasing interest in liatris, particularly as part of a cropping programme alternating with freesias, which occupy the glasshouse in the late autumn to spring, between liatris crops.

Two forms of liatris are grown. Liatris spicata is the more common. This is raised from seed by specialist corm producers, who then sell the corms for flowering in the following year. Corm producers sow seed in April and harvest the corms in the late autumn of the same year.

Such seed-raised corms are the most suitable for cut flower production, as older corms which have flowered the previous season give a much less satisfactory crop. A number of selections of Liatris spicata are offered commercially, which vary in degree of uniformity of colour, shape and flowering time. The original species has a purple-blue flower, and grows to a height of about 70cm. There is also a white variety, Liatris spicata Alba.

The other commercially used species, Liatris callilepis, is a darker blue, and grows rather taller. It is propagated vegetatively, so crops tend to be more uniform, but the cultural requirements are otherwise similar to Liatris spicata.

ESTABLISHMENT

Unlike many summer-flowering crops, liatris has a rather high nutritional requirement. While care should be taken to avoid excessively high salt levels in the soil at planting time, it is still important to maintain adequate levels of the major nutrients. It is not usual to feed once the crop is in growth, particularly with granular materials, because the granules become trapped in the leaf rosette and cause scorching.

When the plant starts to grow strongly it often presents a pale, soft appearance which can be mistaken for nitrogen deficiency. This is quite normal, however, and the crop gradually darkens as it develops. An excess of nitrogen should be avoided, because it encourages too much vigour which in turn favours disease spread.

Liatris is susceptible to verticillium as well as to rhizoctonia root rot and eelworm and it is necessary to include regular soil sterilisation in the growing programme.

Before planting the corms have to have a dormancy-breaking period of cold treatment. This is usually carried out simply by leaving the lifted corms outdoors in trays, since they are quite resistant to frost. Where a cold store is used, the treatment period should be about two months at 2-5C.

Treated corms will generally begin to sprout from the end of March onwards and should be planted by the middle of April. If a retarded crop is being grown the corms are stored cold until they are needed.

Planting density

The planting density of Liatris corms should be related to the corm size and to the growing programme. The smallest corms which can be expected to flower reliably are 5-6cm, each corm yielding a single flower stem of moderate size. A single, heavier flower will be produced by a 6-8cm corm, while larger corms, up to 10cm or more, will yield up to two flower stems per plant.

The corms are planted so that they are only just covered with soil. It is usual to plant through a single layer of wire netting, which can be raised as the flower stems develop to support the blooms in the later stages.

A light dressing of fungicidal dust should be applied after planting but not worked into the ground. The soil should be kept uniformly moist for the first few weeks after planting and spraylines will be helpful in achieving this.

CROP CULTURE

Crops timed to flower from mid-July to about the end of August can be grown in the open or under glass. They are more commonly grown outdoors, because stem strength is rather better. Usual planting date is at the end of the cold treatment, between early March and mid-April, although it is possible to plant at any time from November onwards and to give the cold period after planting.

Clean, strong crops can be left in the ground over winter to crop again for a second year, when they flower rather earlier, from the end of June. This requires soil reasonably free from weeds and free from verticillium disease, to which liatris is susceptible.

Glasshouse conditions

To achieve flowering in the high priced period from mid-May to the end of June requires planting under glass at the end of January or in early February. The corms need to have received sufficient low temperature treatment to ensure uniform growth after planting. Temperatures should be kept at around 10C during March, gradually increasing to 15C as light levels improve. Higher temperatures produce weak growth and a poor quality flower stem.

When ventilating in bright weather, ensure the crop is damped down first because liatris is very susceptible to scorching when humidity is suddenly reduced.

Freeze treatment

Cold-treated corms come into active growth in April and to delay planting after this time to get an autumn crop requires that they should be frozen to prevent their development. This is done by first wetting the corms (by using a fungicidal dip against botrytis and penicillium) then draining the trays before taking them down to a temperature of about -2C.

They are then stored until needed at a low enough temperature that they remain frozen, with visible ice. Individual trays or whole stacks should be draped in plastic film to prevent drying out during storage. The frozen corms are removed from storage about two days before they are needed and then planted as soon as they have thawed out. They should be kept out of direct sunlight until completely thawed.

Planting dates

Retarded crops under glass should be planted between mid-July and the second week of August, to bloom in late October and early November.

Corms can also be planted outdoors in June to flower early October, but crops later than this are less satisfactory, being subject to botrytis in autumn conditions.

Crops grown under glass should be kept as cool as possible during the later summer, aiming for a night temperature around 15C. Good light transmission is essential for reliable flowering so the glass should be kept as clean as possible.

HARVESTING

The blooms are cut when the first few start to show colour. Liatris is unusual in that the blooms open from the top of the stems downwards.

Flowers are graded according to stem length and usually bunched in 10s for presentation to the market. The vase life of liatris can be extended, sometimes doubled, by maintaining a 2.5% or 5% sucrose level in the vase water.

DISEASES

Liatris is particularly susceptible to fungal wilt disease caused by verticillium infection. Verticillium is soil-borne and is also carried in the planting stocks, so it is difficult to eradicate once it is established.

11 Limonium

Annual, generally planted February to April for flowering April to June

The commercial cut flowers or dried flowers known as statice or limonium are mainly selections from the annual species Limonium sinuatum, although the perennial Limonium latifolium is also used. Grown as a biennial from seed, a number of varieties of L sinuatum are available

Although much of the limonium produced commercially at the present time is grown outdoors, there is an increasing interest in culture under glass. Limonium is very dependent on good light and ventilation for good quality blooms, and it is doubtful whether older, poorly ventilated structures will be suitable for this crop.

One potential difficulty is that limonium needs a cold period to induce bud development, and it should be possible to keep the crop at or below 10C for about four weeks during the winter prior to planting out for reliable spring cropping.

Most seed-raisers have developed their own strains of L. sinuatum. These range from the white Alba, through various shades of pink and blue, to deep purples. The Forever series has a range of strong colours and strong tall foliage.

PROPAGATION

Seed of L. sinuatum is sown in trays under glass at around 15C for rapid germination, after which the plants should be hardened off before transplanting.

From sowing to planting out requires about eight to 10 weeks, within which period can be included an intermediate pricking off stage at three to four weeks. The last four weeks prior to planting should be at a temperature of 10C or below to encourage the plants to change over from their juvenile state to flower production.

The planting date, which in turn determines the sowing date, should be related to the required flowering time, and to the likelihood of suitably low outside temperatures for the period of cold treatment. The earliest plantings will be made in January from November sowings.

There is no point in planting after the middle of May, because outdoor production would come at the same time and depress returns below an economic level. On this basis the last sowings should be made at the beginning of March and even these are not practicable if the weather is too warm in April for cold treatment.

CROP CULTURE

Depending on the planting date, it may be necessary to apply a little heat to maintain growth. During January and February a minimum night temperature of 10–12C is adequate, and this should increase as light improves to about 15C in April and May.

The day temperature can be allowed to run up to 20–25C in bright sun before ventilation is given. High humidities must be avoided at all times and particularly during flowering.

Planting density

Plant spacing depends on the earliness of the glasshouse. In older glass with poor light transmission the overall plant density should not be greater than about seven or eight plants/sq m of glasshouse. At this spacing the plants will produce quite strong stems which will not need supporting.

Higher densities, up to 12 plants/sq m, lead to weaker growth with less marketable stems per plant, even though the overall yield per unit area may be higher. The weaker growth which results from close spacings needs some form of support, and a single layer of wire mesh is commonly used.

Nutrition and water

Little specific information is available on the nutritional requirements of limonium. It is usually assumed that for crops grown under glass there are enough residual nutrients so that no base fertilisers or in-crop feeding is needed. It is important to avoid high salt levels in the soil because this is likely to reduce plant vigour to the point where flower stem length is adversely affected.

Limonium should be quite freely watered after planting and the soil kept moist until about three or four weeks before picking starts. From then onwards no water should be applied until the first cut is complete.

Once the first cut is over, a single further application of water may be given, but it is often possible to avoid this if the soil still retains some moisture at depth.

Growing period

The growing period from planting to the end of the first cut is about five or six months, depending on temperature. It is not unusual for growers to clear the crop after the first cut and whether it is worthwhile continuing to produce a second flush depends on the timing of the crop and the likely competition from outdoor crops.

In a good summer the bulk of limonium grown outdoors is sufficient to make continued growth of a glasshouse crop uneconomic, unless the second cut can be

Unlike many of the subjects dealt with in this book, Gypsophila (top) has retained its popularity as a cut flower crop for many years. Liatris on the other hand (right) is one of those which have regained a following thanks largely to the development of techniques to extend its season.

Limonium or Statice is the classic dried flower. It has benefited enomously in recent years from the breeders' attention. Shown here: Limonium Pastel Mixed (above) and Olympic White (right).

[Pictures: Hamer Flower Seeds]

Molucella leavis can be grown outdoors or under glass.

Pinks are very suitable for cropping in a polytunnel (top). They are, in fact, ideal for a small business. Problems associated with the crop include ringspot (above) which can be devastating and which is best avoided, rust (above left) which can be controlled with fungicides, and thrips (left).

[Pictures: H R Whetman & Son]

Breeding has added enormously to the varieties of pinks available. Devon Cream (above) is described as chrome yellow with magenta flush. Joy, which is a high yielding, long-season type, is available in a range of sports (right).

[Pictures: H R Whetman & Son]

Stocks, or Matthiola, need to
be 'doubles' for commercial
production as cut flowers,
like Matthiola Neza Mixed
(above) and Neza Dark Red
(left).

[Pictures: Hamer Flower Seeds]

Like pinks, Sweet William – Dianthus barbatus – are related to carnations. The colour range is impressive, as Neza Mixed (above) illustrates.

Trachelium Midnight (right), one variety of a cut flower type still relatively unknown in the UK.

[Pictures: Hamer Flower Seeds]

delayed to come late in the autumn. On the other hand, a poor summer can reduce the quantity and quality of outdoor limonium to such an extent that good prices can be returned throughout the summer period.

HARVESTING

Cut when the majority of the florets on the stem are showing colour. If the crop is being marketed for drying it is particularly important that harvesting is delayed until at least 75% of the florets are well open.

PESTS AND DISEASES

Botrytis is by far the biggest problem on limonium. It can attack at any time from the propagation stage to flowering, and can cause serious losses if it is allowed to become well established.

Environmental control, as described above, will go a long way towards keeping the crop clean and watering, heating and ventilating techniques should be combined to keep the atmospheric humidity as low as possible at all times.

Chemical control on young plants should be based on dusts, wet sprays and smoke applications of appropriate fungicides.

Aphids can sometimes develop to the point where they need to be controlled chemically. Red spider mite infestations can occur, particularly during the harvesting period when low humidities are common, and these should be controlled with a suitable acaricide applied as a wet spray.

12 Molucella

Annual, planted May to June for flowering July to August

Bells of Ireland, Molucella laevis, is little known as a cut flower crop in the UK, although it now makes a regular appearance in the Dutch auctions. The tall inflorescence is covered with rings of pale green bells, within each of which is a small flower.

Molucella can be grown outside or under glass, the latter technique gaining two or three weeks in time of harvest and so achieving a higher market value. Seed is sown between March and early June.

March sowings are suitable for growing on only with protection, and it is important to keep in mind that the earlier the sowing date the greater the risk of a low germination percentage.

PROPAGATION

Seed can either be sown in rows or broadcast and a seeding rate of 0.5 g/sq m is suitable in either case. It is necessary to thin out the seedlings if a dense stand develops, so there is no point in sowing thickly.

Germination conditions are important and the soil should be kept uniformly moist until emergence is complete. A soil temperature of 20C is ideal but lower temperatures will give satisfactory, if slower, germination.

For culture under glass the young plants should be thinned out to give a final density of about 40 plants/sq m. Few marketable side stems develop at higher plant densities so there is no yield gain.

Thinned plants can be used to transplant but care should be taken to keep these plants moist in warm weather until they are fully re-established, otherwise the check they receive may reduce the yield.

Many growers in Holland buy in young plants from specialist producers to plant out at the same density.

CROP CULTURE

Once the crop is established a minimum temperature of 13C should be maintained day and night as far as practicable and, depending on the season, harvesting will commence in three to three-and-a-half months from sowing. So a March sowing under glass will come into production at the beginning of July.

Crops grown outside should not be sown before April and these are ready to harvest from about the middle of August onwards.

Molucella does not grow well if there are high nutrient levels in the soil and so only minimal base fertiliser applications should be allowed. Liquid feeding will only be needed under deficiency conditions, otherwise they will tend to restrict crop vigour and reduce the marketability of the side-stems.

HARVESTING

The stage of harvesting is determined by the length of the inflorescence rather than by the degree of opening of the flowers. As the flowers develop the stem continues to elongate and it should be cut when the required length is achieved.

After cutting the leaves have to be removed. The lower leaves will break off if the stem is given a sharp shake but the upper leaves have to be cut or snapped off, an operation which is time-consuming but unavoidable. The cut inflorescences should not be stored horizontally or the tips will bend upwards.

DISEASES

Botrytis can be a problem in Molucella particularly for late crops running into damp autumn conditions. In dull weather crop watering should be reduced, and water should be applied early in the day so that the foliage dries as quickly as possible. If heat is available this can be applied with a little ventilation to encourage air movement through the crop. A wet spray of a suitable fungicide can be used to help control an outbreak of botrytis.

The only other common problem of Molucella is sclerotinia, which attacks the base of the plant at soil level. It, too, thrives under moist conditions and cultural control measures are important. Established infection can be treated with a fungicidal soil drench.

13 Pinks

Perennial, from cuttings planted August to flower
late April-November, and March/April to flower
late June-December, with second flush April/May

Pinks, closely related to carnations, have been grown successfully under cold
glass and polytunnels for some 30 years. They provide an ideal crop for a small
family business. It costs relatively little to grow the crop, it needs no special equip-
ment and requires no heat, and a small business is flexible enough to cope with the
labour peaks.

Pinks go on cropping for 18 months, that being the optimum to maintain quality
blooms, especially the variety Doris. During that time a sequence of three quite distinct flushes will be produced, separated by a semi-dormant phase during the winter.

The time of planting used to depend on whether heat was available. Nowadays
the price premium for early crops is insufficient to justify heating, except for frost
protection. In fact pinks grow very successfully in cold glass or polytunnels.

There are two main planting times. Plant in August to flower from late April to
November, and between March and April to flower from late June to December with
a second flush in April and May.

A good rotation for pinks is to alternate between August and spring planting with
sterilisation in November/December or July respectively. Following the spring
planting there is a semi-dormant period through the winter then a final flush is taken
in May and June of the second year, followed by crop clearance.

Even in cold structures it is possible to plant outside the more common sched-
ules, although low light levels and temperatures during the winter prevent successful establishment between the beginning of November and late February.

The young plants should always be stopped once, soon after planting, to encourage lateral shoots which provide the first crop.

Varieties

For years the standard pinks variety was Doris and it is still the most popular. It is a light salmon in colour with a dark ring. Its main drawback is its tendency to crop in flushes which can cause labour and marketing problems and the quality deteriorates rapidly in the warmer months of June to August. Joy is a good alternative to Doris; it crops as well but over a much longer season with comparable yields.

For the wholesale market the returns achieved give growers little incentive to produce anything but pink varieties as the trade seems to take little interest in the product as such. However where the flowers can be sold direct, either to the retailer or consumer, it will be well worth growing a range of colours, a varied display encouraging sales.

Most modern varieties also flower over a prolonged period helping to provide the continuity of supply essential for direct sales. Some varieties that can be recommended are shown in the table.

Joy	carmine pink
Claret Joy	bright pink
Rose Joy	purple pink
White Joy	very pale pink becoming white on opening
Devon Cream	chrome yellow, magenta flush
Devon General	bright carmine
Pink Devon Pearl	soft pink
Devon Wizard	purple
Monica Wyatt	phlox pink
Rose Monica Wyatt	pale pink, carmine centre
Letitia Wyatt	carmine pink

Most of these varieties have the characteristic clove fragrance of pinks, except for Joy, Claret Joy and Devon Cream which are poorly scented. All produce double blooms and consequently last longer than semi-double varieties like Doris.

Cuttings

These days pinks are propagated almost exclusively by specialist propagators who probably account for 99% of commercial production. These specialists root the cuttings as plug plants which allow the grower to concentrate on cropping and marketing the blooms.

In selecting a source of young plants it is a wise precaution to specify that they come from parent stock obtained from the Nuclear Stock Association. Insisting on plants of NSA origin will go a long way in preventing the introduction of viruses.

Cuttings production is not difficult but the need to obtain a healthy stock true to the variety is paramount.

ESTABLISHMENT

If the growing on house is ready, the rooted cuttings can be moved directly into their final positions at this stage.

If they are to be held before planting out, they should be moved into pots containing a potting compost, either soil or peat based. Until planting potted-up plants should be kept in a cool situation in good light, and stopped by snapping out the central shoot as soon as it has elongated enough to be easily handled.

The border soil into which pinks are planted should be weed-free, and likely to remain reasonably so for 18 months so soil sterilisation will often be needed to eliminate perennial weeds. If pinks or related crops – including carnations – have been previously grown in the same soil, thorough sterilisation is particularly important.

Pinks, like carnations, prefer a rather alkaline soil and the pH should be raised to at least 6.7 by the addition of lime if necessary.

Young plants should be planted into moist soil. Depth of planting does not seem critical with pinks.

Planting density

The planting density should be related to the time of the year. Summer plantings make a lot of early growth and can be put in at 30 x 30cm. Late autumn plantings can be much closer, at 20 x 20cm, while early autumn plantings can be at an intermediate density.

As the plants start to make new growth they tend to spread across the bed, and some form of wire support or kick board will be needed to prevent the plants at the edge of the bed from encroaching on the path.

CROP CULTURE

Watering the crop is best done by a ground-level system like seep hose rather than overhead spraylines as the foliage is kept dry with a consequent reduction in leaf diseases. Such systems are also more economic in terms of fertiliser use and produce a better quality product.

The frequency and volume of individual waterings will vary widely with the time of year and with the soil type and drainage. The aim should be to maintain a fairly uniform level of moisture in the soil. During the growing system the crop should never be allowed to dry out or yield and quality will suffer. Pinks can be kept quite dry, however, from November to February.

If overhead irrigation is used, water should be applied early in the day to give the foliage time to dry off by nightfall.

Liquid feed should be applied with every watering, unless soil analysis indicates an excessive build-up of nutrients. As a general rule a feed supplying 150-200ppm each of nitrogen and potassium is suitable. Because pinks are sensitive to boron deficiency, borax should occasionally be incorporated into the liquid feed.

Temperatures

As mentioned earlier, the economics of pinks production no longer justify heating except for frost protection. On the other hand high summer temperatures should be avoided as they quickly reduce flower quality. High humidities can also be a serious problem during the autumn and minimal watering must be combined with maximum ventilation to keep the crop and environment as dry as possible.

In mid-winter the crop can be allowed to freeze, unless there happens to be a lot of bud present. At other times free ventilation should be the rule, especially in polytunnels to avoid condensation; side netting is a valuable aid in this context.

Supplementary lighting

Like carnations pinks respond well to a period of supplementary lighting during the break elongation stage, lighting from when the shoots have five or six pairs of leaves. Like heating, however, it is unlikely to be justified at today's level of return and quality is indifferent.

HARVESTING

Pinks should be harvested early in the day so that they can be conditioned in deep water in a cool place for several hours before being packed. The blooms are ready to harvest when the petals have just split and the flowers are beginning to open.

It is essential to include some form of post-harvest treatment. Proprietary materials containing silver thiosulphate can be used or the chemical can be made up on the nursery. Given for five hours at ambient temperatures or 24 hours at +2C can double the vase life of cut blooms.

Packing pinks as faced bunches is too labour intensive; the bunches also take up too much room in the box. Posy bunches with the heads together look better when displayed in buckets by the retailer.

In a two-year crop 60% of the crop will be harvested in the first year but better quality will translate this into 70% of net income.

Labour needs

Labour peaks can be reduced by growing a wide range of modern perpetual flowering varieties. The labour requirements for harvesting and marketing should not be underestimated. Total labour needs will be around 240 hours/100sq m and of this figure 200 hours represents harvesting, bunching and packing. Since as much as 75 hours of this can be taken up in the first flush alone it is clear that peak labour demand can be very high and unless casual labour is available it is necessary to consider how such an unbalanced labour profile can be made to fit into the overall nursery programme.

PESTS AND DISEASES

Pinks are generally susceptible to the same range of diseases as carnations, of which fusarium wilt (caused by F. oxysporum f.s. dianthi) is potentially the most important. This fungus invades the conducting tissue of plants and causes wilting and death by blocking conduction of water and nutrients.

F. oxysporum f.s. dianthi is a problem on sites where pinks or carnations have been grown for some time, and there is nothing practicable that can be done to eradicate it. It is seldom seen on new sites, provided NSA stock is planted.

Cuttings are another potential source of infection underlining the need to check the status of parent material. Plants showing wilt symptoms should be promptly removed from the house and a thorough soil sterilisation programme, preferably by steaming, carried out.

Fusarium avenaceum and F. culmorum are common problems where the plants have had some sort of check at any early stage of growth. Causes include hard cuttings, extreme waterlogging or dryness at any time from sticking the cutting to establishing the young plant, high salinity and low pH. The problems are aggravated by high temperature which favours the development of Fusarium spp. The disease manifests itself as a basal rot causing the young plant to collapse, older plants dying back gradually into the crown. Benomyl fungicides may give some measure of control.

Leaf diseases

Leaf diseases can be a severe problem with overhead watering, particularly during the autumn and winter and where ventilation is inadequate.

Carnation rust (Uromyces dianthi) can be controlled with fungicides.

Ringspot (Mycosphaerella dianthi) can devastate the crop rendering the blooms unsaleable and destroying the foliage. Symtoms are tan coloured spots with purple-brown margins. With this disease fungicides are only partially successful.

The fungus Heteropetella valtellinensis is usually only a problem in outdoor crops.

Cultural control measures play an important part in reducing the impact of both stub rot and the major leaf diseases. Free, vigorous growth is less likely to succumb to infection than plants which have received a check to growth or which failed to establish quickly after planting.

Viruses

A number of viruses, such as carnation necrotic fleck virus and carnation mottle virus, affect carnations and pinks alike but virus should not be a problem provided plants are obtained from a propagator using NSA-inexed mother plants on an annual replacement basis and provided there is no other infected material on the holding.

Aphid vectors are easily controlled (the commonest way viruses are transmitted is through inoculation by sap on workers' hands).

Aphids are in fact the most common pest problem of pinks. Red spider mite can be a serious summer pest which rapidly becomes resistant to acaricides, often because of ineffictive spraying techniques. Predators provide a viable alternative control, provided onion thrip is also controlled.

14 Stocks

Annual, from seed, flowering from April to June

Also referred to as Matthiola, interest in stocks for cut flower work has increased recently with the introduction of better selections for glasshouse production. The best quality will be achieved with medium-early selections. Early sorts will come into flower more quickly, but at the expense of shorter stems and lower quality.

For the production of cut flower stocks under glass it is necessary to use the so-called 100% double strains. These are actually a misnomer, because a proportion of the seedlings will develop into single blooms. However these are quite easily identified at the time of pricking off and can be discarded at that stage.

Stocks are most commonly grown to flower from late March through to about June although it is also possible to crop in November and December. The earliest crops are planted out in December from sowings made during October, and require some heat input to bring them into flower during the early spring.

Later sowings, in November and December, can be transplanted in February or March to flower later in the spring with little or no heat. Winter crops should be sown during late July, and planted out during September.

PROPAGATION

A gram of seed will yield about 150 double-flowering plants after selection, and the quantity of seed needed should be based on a spacing of about 13 x 13cm. Seed should be sown thinly in trays, and a temperature of 18-20C should be maintained at first to ensure rapid and uniform emergence.

As soon as the seedlings are visible the temperature can be dropped to 10C for winter sowings. High temperatures can be a problem with summer sowings, and germination will be inhibited if the compost temperature regularly exceeds about 20C.

Singling out

The segregation of single- and double-flowering plants relies on low temperatures to bring out the colour differences between the two types of plants. For winter sowings it is often enough to allow the air temperature to drop below 10C after emergence but if this is not possible then the trays of seedlings should be put into a cold store at about 7-8C for two or three days.

Following this treatment it will be apparent that some seedlings are noticeably darker than the others. These are singles and they should be discarded at this stage. The lighter-coloured seedlings are doubles. These can either be planted out directly into the cropping house or pricked off into small containers.

CROP CULTURE

Stocks prefer a rather alkaline soil, with a pH in the range 6.5 to 7.0. The plants must be grown quite hard for good bloom colour and to reduce the risk of botrytis infection, and so a good level of potassium should be provided in the base fertiliser, whereas nitrogen levels should be kept low.

Watering and feeding

Stocks are susceptible to stem rot, particularly during damp conditions in the winter, and so the crop should be watered carefully and infrequently at this time. Water should be applied whenever the soil show signs of drying back, because any check in growth will reduce the quality of the blooms. Hose watering is preferred to overhead sprays at all times and particularly as the crop approaches flowering.

Liquid feeding is not usually needed if adequate base fertilisers have been provided, and if soil analysis indicates a deficiency a feed with a high ratio of potassium to nitrogen should be used to keep the growth hard.

Temperature regime

If heat is available winter crops will benefit from maintaining a minimum air temperature of 12-14C, although stocks can be grown through successfully at rather lower temperatures than this, if diseases are kept under control. High temperatures are likely to result in a low quality product with fewer flower buds per stem.

The most important aspect of culture in the winter is to keep plenty of air movement through the crop and to ventilate freely whenever outside conditions permit. In the spring and early summer ventilation should be continuous in warm weather, and the temperatures kept as low as practicable.

HARVESTING

Stocks are harvested when the bottom three blooms on the spike have opened, although a slightly more advanced spike is acceptable for local marketing.

It is usual to cut the whole plant at soil level, and then to strip off the lower leaves to leave about 10cm of bare stem at the base. Spikes are commonly bunched in fives, although large blooms are still sometimes presented in threes.

PESTS AND DISEASES

Few pests become established on stocks, although aphids are a fairly regular problem. The usual range of insecticides will give control. Red spider mite can damage the leaves, so reducing the quality of the spike, and should be treated promptly.

Diseases

Rhizoctonia stem rot is a common disease of stocks, particularly when inadequate soil sterilisation has been carried out. Steaming is necessary to eradicate rhizoctonia from soil once it has become established. It is a worthwhile added precaution to incorporate a fungicidal dust into the surface layers of soil before planting out.

The risk of rhizoctonia attacking the plants is less if damp conditions around the base of the stem are avoided, and overhead damping down should not normally be continued once the young plants are established in their cropping positions. Established infection may be controlled with wet sprays of a fungicide, applied in sufficient volume to reach the base of the plants.

Downy mildew often attacks the leaves, and this disease too is more likely to be a problem in damp, under-ventilated crops. Routine high volume wet sprays of a suitable fungicide should prevent downy mildew from becoming established in the crop.

15 Sweet william

Biennial, from seed sown in July for flowering the following May or June

Sweet william, Dianthus barbatus, is closely related to carnations, and can be forced under suitable cultural conditions to give an early, profitable crop under glass or plastic. The original sweet william is a biennial which is sown early in July, overwintered and brought into bloom in May and June the following year. These types are less commonly grown from cuttings to bring them into flower in late autumn.

A wide range of biennial varieties are offered by seedsmen, sometimes classified as early, mid-season and late. The best choice of colours can generally be found in the later varieties. It is not necessary to sow separate colours, as the market generally accepts good mixed bunches most readily.

There are also a number of hybrids which do not need overwintering to bring them into flower, so they can be grown as annuals. They can be sown from late spring onwards to start flowering in the autumn.

These types are perpetual flowering, and remain in production until low winter temperatures and light curtail their growth. Some high quality F1 hybrids are starting to become available now, and there are also some vegetatively propagated varieties, developed in Israel, which come into flower early without a period of low temperatures.

PROPAGATION

Any open, well-drained soil is suitable for this crop, although it is sensitive to high salt levels, and care should be taken to leach any excess nutrients before planting. Sweet william is particularly sensitive to bromide residues, and it is necessary to leach the soil well if methyl bromide has been used as a soil sterilant. Base fertilisers will not normally be needed unless soil analysis indicates a particular deficiency.

Sowing timetable

Seed can be sown in the flowering area, but this is wasteful of glasshouse time, and it is more usual to sow in prepared seedbeds outdoors or under glass for later transplanting. The sowing date should be within the first two weeks of July if a forcing programme is to be followed.

Earlier sowing produces a plant which is too vigorous, and susceptible to botrytis and other problems. Late sowing does not allow the plant to build up enough vegetative growth before the winter.

Sowings under glass should be lightly shaded, and perhaps also covered with hessian to maintain soil moisture until germination is complete. For direct sowing use an equivalent weight of seed, sowing in rows, and thinning out to the required spacing with the rows after emergence.

ESTABLISHMENT

Plants raised in seed beds should be transplanted into their final positions early in the autumn. Dense sowings should be moved as early as mid-August, while thinner stands can safely wait until the second half of September.

If the soil type encourages vigorous growth it is better not to transplant too early, as dense foliage will increase the risk of botrytis and rust becoming established during the winter.

CROP CULTURE

Sweet william is daylength sensitive. It will only initiate flower buds under long day conditions.

It is also necessary to subject the biennial strains to a period of low temperature (vernalisation) between the vegetative growth of the first season and the flower development of the second. These two requirements form the basis of the forcing recommendations.

For maximum forcing the sowing should not be delayed. It is important to build up a strong plant before the winter, because early blooms can only develop well on a fully-grown vegetative shoot. The young plants should ideally be transplanted at first outdoors and then moved under glass, with root-ball attached, at the end of December.

Heat and light

They must be grown cold throughout January with a maximum temperature of 5C at night and 10C during the day.

At the beginning of February heating is begun, allowing a maximum of 12C at night for the first month. At the same time artificial lighting is given to the crop between dusk and dawn for about two and a half weeks.

A low level of illumination, similar to that used for carnations, is adequate and a level of 15 watts/sq m of bed, uniformly distributed, is enough.

As the natural light levels improve into the spring, temperatures can gradually be raised to a final level of 15C, or a bit more in bright sun.

If mobile houses are available these are particularly suited to forcing sweet william, because the crop can be covered only at the start of the heating and lighting phase, so reducing the risk of botrytis and other fungal diseases becoming established during the winter.

Because of the risk of diseases such as botrytis it may be necessary to apply a little heat with ventilation in the late autumn if humid conditions persist. Watering should be reduced through the winter and only applied, if possible, when the crop can be dried off by dusk. Overhead spraylines are most commonly used.

It has not been established whether carbon dioxide enrichment on sweet william would give an economic advantage. It should be possible to run temperatures rather higher through the forcing period if carbon dioxide enrichment were being employed, because there would be less risk of bud abortion in low light conditions, but this has not been put to the test under commercial conditions.

HARVESTING

Sweet william should be harvested when a few blooms are open. It is usual to make up bunches of mixed colour.

The number of stems does not have to be consistent. It is more important to make up a uniform volume of bunch.

The first cuts are generally quite heavy, and 10 stems/bunch make a good pack, while the size of later cuts can be very variable.

PESTS AND DISEASES

Sweet william is particularly prone to a number of diseases, of which botrytis and rust are the most common. Botrytis can spread quickly through the crop in the dull, damp conditions of winter and it is important to regulate the environment to reduce its activity.

The foliage should be kept as dry as possible at all times, particularly at night, and ventilation and pipe heat applied in humid conditions to maintain air movement through the crop. Excessively dense foliage through the winter should be avoided by not planting too early if the soil conditions are known to encourage vigorous growth.

Unlike botrytis rust is a disease which is specific to sweet william and related plants. It is caused by the fungus Uromyces dianthi, which spreads in the same conditions which favour the establishment of botrytis. It is therefore necessary to apply the same cultural control measures aimed at reducing moisture and humidity. Precautionary fungicidal sprays can be applied in the autumn if an attack of rust is anticipated on the basis of past experience.

Sweet william occasionally become attacked by one of a pair of fungi (Septonia dianthi, Heteropatella valtellinensis) which cause spotting of the foliage. They can be controlled by fungicidal sprays of a suitable material.

Several pests can attack sweet william, including aphids, slugs and white fly chemical control is available using any of the normal range of pesticides.

16 Trachelium

Annual, from seed

Trachelium coeruleum is an annual which is grown from seed for summer flowering. It is a long-day plant which is usually sown between September and May for planting out between November and late June. Trachelium is still more or less unknown in the UK, but in Europe and Japan it is gaining rapidly in importance as its attractive shape and long vase life become more widely recognised.

There are several selections of Trachelium available in the UK already, but so far these are mainly variations in colour from white through pale blue to dark blue. All of these reach a height of around 80-90cm at flowering. As the popularity of Trachelium increases there will certainly be a wider range of better quality varieties making their appearance.

PROPAGATION
Trachelium is grown from seed. At the optimum germination and propagation temperature of 20C seedlings will be ready for transplanting in six to eight weeks from a late spring sowing, or up to three months after sowing in late autumn. In Holland young plants raised in plugs can be bought in from specialist producers.

CROP CULTURE
Plants should be spaced at about 50/sq m of glasshouse if the crop is to be taken up to flowering on single stems, or at 25-35/sq m if the plants are going to be pinched.

A night temperature of 15-16C is suitable to maintain active growth.

No particular nutritional requirements have been reported for cut flower crops, although research on pot plant production in Germany has identified trachelium as having quite a high fertiliser requirement. It is also known that the crop is sensitive to manganese toxicity, which can cause severe leaf scorch, so care should be taken to avoid manganese release into the soil if it is steam sterilised directly before planting.

The natural flowering season for trachelium is June and July. Buds will start to initiate as soon as the daylength reaches 15 hours in mid-May. This means that seed should be sown by March at the latest to get enough height on an unpinched crop before the plants switch to flower development.

A January start is more appropriate if the plants are to be pinched. In either case the plants should be encouraged into vigorous growth in early May by applying plenty of water and some liquid feed.

Daylength control

It is possible to advance flowering on an early-sown crop by lighting from two weeks after sowing or pinching. Lighting to give 16-hour days is needed and the treatment should be continued until mid-May or until the start of flowering, whichever comes first. Incandescent lights are best and cyclic lighting of 10 minutes in every half hour is effective as is five-hour night-break lighting.

Late-started crops can be prevented from flowering too quickly by shading to reduce daylength down to below 12 hours. Provisional recommendations are that shading should continue until mid-July or until the plants reach a height of 15-20cm. Flowering will then occur between mid August and early October.

HARVESTING

Although it is usual to take only a single flush, it is possible to cut down an early-flowering crop in early July to get a second flush in the autumn. Cutting too high will generate too many weak shoots, while cutting too low will kill many of the plants, so this operation is quite critical.

The crop should be well watered before cutting, because the plants are likely to suffer from rots if water is applied afterwards on to the cut stems. Heavy shading in July and early August is necessary to get adequate stem length on the second flush, and even then the production and quality will be very variable.

Trachelium should not be cut until at least three or four flowers are open, otherwise the remaining buds will not all open fully. The cut stems should be moved quickly into water in a cool place to minimise wilting.

When the cut flowers are sleeved the flower canopy must remain above the top edge of the sleeve, otherwise botrytis infection will spread on the opening flowers and spoil them.